A STUDY OF MAN

AND

THE WAY TO HEALTH

BY

J. D. BUCK, M. D.

————

Selfishness is the father of vice;
Altruism, the mother of virtue.

————

New Edition, Revised and Enlarged

————

CHICAGO
INDO-AMERICAN BOOK CO.
5705 W. Lake St.
1914

DEDICATION.

To the pure Light of Love
That beams on the altar of my home
And to the inspiring Soul of Unselfishness
That radiates from the life of my sister
These pages are affectionately inscribed.

FOREWORD.

The following volume was designed to lead up to a systematic, and, therefore, a scientific and philosophical study of man. With Religion on the one side, and materialistic Science on the other, with the average individual no provision was made in current beliefs or the annals of science for a rational conception of the human soul.

Between faith without reason, and reason, under the garb of science, without faith, agnosticism was being insidiously transformed into a soulless and Godless materialism. Problems the most vital to man were labeled "Unknowable." So-called science virtually declared the quest for the soul altogether visionary and did its best and its utmost to discourage the search altogether.

The Study of Man was designed to show the Modulus that underlies the whole nature of man. Emphasizing the facts of common experiences, and avoiding all theorizing as far as possible, the facts cognizant to all were allowed to tell their own story, and thus reveal the obvious and necessary inferences. Consciousness was thus shown as compassing equally, a natural and a spiritual world, in the common experience of man. No effort whatever was made to construct a theory of the soul, but it was designed to lessen the force of agnosticism by suggestions of a possible Gnosis, and to counteract the blighting curse of materialism by showing man to be essentially a spiritual being.

Moreover, the inference is very general, and everywhere upheld by the language and theories of modern science, that the higher evolution of man consists in and is determined by intellectual development, and the ethical or moral element is included by courtesy. Then by making all intellectual processes adhere strictly as a function of the physical brain, this Physio-psychology, synonymous with all mental processes, again closed the cycle of materialism. It was attempted, without direct reference to these materialistic theories, to so present the facts of common experience, as to make these materialistic theories forever more impossible, by showing the modulus of man to involve a two-fold life in the form of a universal and exact equation.

Thus the outer world of things, and the inner world of ideas: the objective and the subjective, the Natural and the Spiritual, were shown to adhere equally in all human experience, and to be the modulus of Nature, everywhere manifest in the life of man.

The working hypothesis of modern physical science undertakes to reduce all problems in the life of man, as in physical nature at large, to terms of mass and motion.

In the Kinetics of the physical brain and nervous mechanism Science finds its psychical theorem. The phenomena of thought and the relation between structure and function may be observed, studied, classified, *ad infinitum*, and yet, if the fact of *consciousness* is belittled or ignored, man will never grasp the real problem of the soul, or arrive at any adequate theorem of the higher evolution.

The human is essentially the humane. All intellectual processes that overlook or ignore simple kindness or compassion are inhuman, to say the least, and can alone never determine the higher evolution of man. Hence the principle of altruism is shown to underlie all problems in the life of man. This adheres from the modulus of Nature, and the overshadowing of the Divine from which the life of man proceeds.

During the past decade these altruistic principles and concepts have gained immeasurably in the attention and conscience of our fellowmen. Scientific Materialism so-called has proportionately loosened its hold. Wireless telegraphy has suggested new concepts in nature's finer forces. The trend of thought and the lines of interest have, in many directions, moved to higher planes. The two planes of consciousness in man everywhere recognized in this book and continually appealed to as basic in all phenomena of conscious life, are now quite generally recognized; whereas, when this book first appeared they were more often scouted or ridiculed by so-called scientists. Prof. William James of Harvard declares "the Subconscious Self to be, nowadays, a *well-accredited physchological entity.*" It will presently be recognized that it is the supraconscious Self, rather than the sub-conscious, that must be recognized in all the higher groups of psychic phenomena. In this book the term Higher Self was used to designate the ego as the adjunct in these higher phenomena. Hence we have the Conscious

Self, the Sub-conscious Self, the Supra-conscious Self, three aspects of the Ego representing three well-marked planes of consciousness.

In the chapter on Planes of Life it was undertaken to illustrate these planes of consciousness without formulating the philosophy upon which the conception rests, except by the broadest generalizations.

It is thus easy to show that great progress is being made, and along what lines.

The text of the book remains as first written. The author has no alterations to make.

It may here be said in passing, however, that the terms "dead matter" and "living matter" were used at the time in the conventional sense of modern physiology, while in the chapters on Life and Living Forms, Life is regarded as potential or latent in all matter. As a quality Life is an Ultimate, like Consciousness, Law, etc.

In the process of nutrition and assimilation, so-called "dead matter" is constantly being converted into living tissue, and this is inconceivable if a radical difference between them really exists. It is evidently the same substance under different conditions, what we call Life being latent in the one case and manifest or active in the other.

With the Higher Criticism in religious matters, and the recognition of the Finer Forces in scientific research, there is a very evident up-lift toward spiritual discernment. Materialism in science and creed and dogma in religion are thus giving place to the New Psychology. This Science of the Soul recognizes the innate spiritual intuitions as the true illuminator of man, which all true science confirms, and all true religion fosters and assists.

The Study of Man was originally designed to lead up to, and facilitate just this spiritual enlightenment by those general considerations that make it both logical and unavoidable.

All our conclusions regarding the nature, the mission, and the destiny of man, depend on the point from which we view him. If we regard him as simply an "improved animal" we shall strive in vain to account for or to apprehend his higher faculties and transcendent powers.

But if we regard man as essentially a spiritual being from our higher vantage-ground his lower nature and all the intervening planes of consciousness may be clearly apprehended. Hence the Natural and the Spiritual are herein shown to be basic in our theorem of Life, the process of evolution and involution to be an underlying vital equation, and the Perfect Man alike the Ideal of Universal Nature and Divine Intelligence.

J. D. B.

December, 1903.

PREFACE.

"Know then thyself, presume not God to scan;
The proper study of mankind is man.
Placed on this isthmus of a middle state,
A being darkly wise, and rudely great;
With too much knowledge for the skeptic side,
With too much weakness for the Stoic's pride,
He hangs between; in doubt to act, or rest;
In doubt to deem himself a god, or beast;
In doubt his mind or body to prefer;
Born but to die, and reasoning but to err;
Alike in ignorance, his reasoning such,
Whether he thinks too little or too much;
Chaos of thought and passion, all confused;
Still by himself abused or disabused;
Created half to rise, or half to fall;
Great lord of all things, yet a prey to all;
Sole judge of truth, in endless error hurl'd,
The glory, jest and riddle of the world!"

Such was man as viewed through the eyes of Alexander Pope. But few of the present generation read Pope, and yet mankind is much the same now as two hundred years ago, and for the average individual these famous lines are as true now as when they were first penned.

There have been those in all ages who have devoted their lives to the study of man, and these have at least apprehended the nature of the problems involved in its origin, nature, and destiny, though they may have been unable to solve them. Most wonderful progress has indeed been made in material things during the past two hundred years, and more especially during the last half century; yet man is still

"The glory, jest and riddle of the world!"

There never was a time in the history of letters when so great facilities and so few barriers were presented to the study of man as now. Investigation is to-day practically free. There are no barriers to any study that does not interfere directly with the life, liberty and happiness of another. There may, indeed, be found a lurking remnant of the old persecution, but fortunately it is seldom marshaled in the name of religion. It rather issues from the camp of the nihilist as a rather mild form of ridicule of him who ventures to question the realm scientifically dubbed the unknowable. Yet even here the progress of science in the realm of nature's finer forces has been so great that the majority of really earnest and intelligent persons declare that they are not prepared to say what is possible and what not, and that they would hardly be surprised at anything. Among the really devout and earnest souls it is usually enough that one earnestly seeks the truth for the benefit of man in order to enlist attention and courteous examination. The motto of these is anything that is right and true for the benefit of humanity. It is true that there does not appear on the surface of things nowadays so great solicitude for the glory of God, for the reason that it has been discerned in these later times that the glory of God depends on the elevation of man; for only as man's thoughts are purified and his life elevated can he seek and adore the source of all life, the bestower of all good, and the fountain of all truth.

Opportunities for observing human nature in all its modes of life, in every degree of development, and in every clime, were never so great as they are to-day. One may now circumnavigate the globe with less expenditure of time and money than would have been required a few years ago to cross a continent or a principality

Railroads and telegraphs have consolidated humanity. If a flood occurs in the Celestial Empire, a cyclone in Ceylon, or if two emperors meet on neutral ground to discuss the fate of empires, and to consider the propriety of allowing a few thousands of their subjects to slaughter each other, we read of all these things in the daily press over our coffee the next morning. We are almost able to feel the pulse and note the daily temperature of a sick and bedoctored emperor on the other side of the globe, and we are apprised of his demise before the services of the wrangling physicians have given place to those of the Royal undertaker.

From the wonderful advancement in the art of printing have come the multiplication of books, the reproduction of ancient manuscripts, the progress of science and the arts and the general diffusion of learning, thus placing these treasures within reach of the poorest, giving them facilities once the birthright of kings only. Priceless volumes are stored in public libraries, accessible to any who will use and not destroy; while to the halls of learning the price of admission is learning itself, rather than the favor of princes.

We have seen doctrines, as evolution, which were at first supposed to be subversive of all truth and righteousness, make such rapid progress that a single decade was sufficient to make them popular wherever comprehended, and where another decade found them involved in pulpit utterance as the criterion of intelligence. Religion is no longer afraid of her altars in the presence of anything that can be shown to be true and beneficent, while the dark shadow that once glowered over her altars and quenched her sacred fires has fled at the approach of the illuminating angel of humanity. Just in proportion as superstition recedes, does peace and good will to

man advance. No odium theologicum attaches to any **depart-**
ment of learning, and no utterance made by a thoughtful
mind and set forth with candor and decency excites either
surprise or alarm. A stronger weapon than even persecution
is now recognized, namely, intelligent criticism and disproof.

Modern science has pushed its investigations into every department of nature. It has dredged the deepest seas, scaled
the highest mountains, analyzed the sunbeam, and resolved
the distant nebula. Science has rendered the hardest metals
incandescent, and seems only to be gathering breath, and
strength before it dissolves the elements. Science has thus
pushed experiment and analysis, instituted comparisons, weighed,
measured, tabulated, systematized and recorded **facts.**

In all this investigation no external kingdom of nature has
been overlooked, nor escaped the argus-eyed explorer. The
habits, modes of origin and cycles of life of plants and animals
have been observed over a large part of the habitable globe,
while organisms whose theater of life is invisible to the naked
eye have been studied under the microscope until they are as
familiar to the biologist as household words; and while the
brave Stanley, worthy successor to Livingston, is lost in the
jungles of Africa the ambitious Arctic explorer dreams of an
open polar sea.

Comparative anatomy and comparative physiology have
greatly enlarged our knowledge of the theater, the mechanism and the phenomena of life, while these, together with the
study of the zoophite and the amoeba, have added greatly to
our knowledge of the structure and functions of life in man.

The study of sociology has been undertaken with zeal and
intelligence, thus furnishing future students valuable material,
if not final results.

The last stronghold of superstition and ignorance is the psychical nature of man. While the problems in psychology are
the last and the most difficult to be investigated, they give at

the same time the most curious interest to the ignorant, and
excite in the intelligent the greatest diversity of opinion.
It might therefore be said of psychology, and might be applied to most of the discussions thereon, as it was once said of
philosophy: they are treatises on a subject that no one knows
any thing about, conducted in a language that no one under-
stands. The reason for this condition of things may, perhaps,
be shown in the following pages. There is certainly no lack of
facts, no dearth of materials, upon which to build the foundations, at least, of a science of psychology. The author of
this work trusts that it may appear in the sequel that only better
methods are needed to bring about the desired result. All such
investigations may indeed proceed from a physical basis, though
they all transcend physics. They may also be conducted scientifically, but must also be supplemented by synthetic processes to be derived only from a sound and far-reaching philosophy. All higher knowledge is a consensus of all experience;
for man, therefore, in any true sense to know his higher nature he must have reached that plane first by experience.
The experience of man has reached, at least in many cases,
the threshold of the higher knowledge. Recorded and oft-
verified observations and experiments are not wanting; while
to rare psychological phenomena may also be added almost
universal individual experience—incidents which seem to transcend the known laws of physics, and which have not been
properly assigned and apprehended for lack of a knowledge of
any law governing them. Science has all along attempted to
convert subjective experience into terms of phenomenal existence, and it could not be otherwise than that such experience
thus dragged out of place should appear distorted and fantastic, and should refuse to yield definite results. Moreover,
that which is at best a method of procedure has been mistaken for a result, and the dictum of science, prejudging events
and preventing equitable measure of facts, bids fair to accom-

plish for science what superstition has done for religion, namely, to place authority over truth.

With this condition of things thus briefly outlined what more important and interesting field for investigation presents itself to the earnest student than the entire nature of man? The great social problems that vex mankind await these investigations. The principles of capital and labor, the social evil, the enfranchisement of woman, and the great principles of al· truism and egotism that underlie all others, clamor for solution, and these can never be fully determined except on a strict basis of law that takes cognizance of every fact in phys-iology and every principle of a true psychology; and to arrive at these man requires more real knowledge of himself. The author of these pages hopes to be able to show that a better method in the use of the materials already on hand will lead up to just this knowledge, and at least will outline those prin-ciples that underlie the entire nature of man.

It is often asserted that the study of medicine leads to athe-ism, and that a very large number of physicians are therefore atheists. The study of medicine is in its broadest sense the study of man in all his relations and manifestations. It might easily be shown that the proportion of atheists and material-ists among physicians is by no means greater than among any other class of persons of equal culture and education. If, however, it be really true that the study of man necessarily leads to atheism, then it follows that ignorance of one's own nature is but another name for theism, and that only the ig-norant can believe in God. If there be danger in the direc-tion indicated, it is the little learning that is the dangerous thing. If the study of man extends only to surface problems, as is too often the case, and is concerned only with sufficient learning to enable one to write a prescription and collect a fee, then the result here as elsewhere may be atheism, as the pur-suit is measured by self-interest. Strictly speaking, the study of man has no more to do with the question of theism proper than has the study of nature. Theism is an element in pantheism; for, as shown in the following pages, man's idea of God is drawn equally from nature, and from human nature.

The object of this work is to show that there is a modulus in nature and a divinity in man, and that these two are in essence one, and that therefore God and nature are not at cross-purposes.

In pursuing the subject from its physical side only the barest outlines of physics and physiology have been attempted, sufficient, however, to show the method suggested and the line of investigation to be pursued.

The writer of this book has been for many years deeply interested in all that relates to human nature, or that promises in any way to mitigate human suffering and increase the sum of human happiness. He has no peculiar views that he desires to impress on any one, but he believes that a somewhat different use of facts and materials already in our possession will give a deeper insight into human nature, and will secure far more satisfactory results than are usually attained. He believes that while traversing old ground, he has herein suggested the exploration of it in a new way, though by no means original with himself; and he is not aware of any previous attempt at the reconciliation of Science and Religion on the basis herein proposed. This reconciliation lies in the logical application of one universal law that is coincident with all nature and commensurate with all life. This law does not subvert, but supplements the theory of evolution, by involution, and recognizes all processes of creation, or of being, as equations, the modulus of which is the underlying cosmic duality.

This treatise may be epitomized as follows:

The cosmic form in which all things are created, and in which all things exist, is a universal duality.

Involution and evolution express the twofold process of the one law of development, corresponding to the two planes of being, the subjective and the objective. Consciousness is the central fact of being.

Experience is the only method of knowing; therefore to know is to become.

The Modulus of Nature, that is, the pattern after which she everywhere builds, and the method to which she continually conforms, is an Ideal or Archetypal Man.

The Perfect Man is the anthropomorphic God, a living, present Christ in every human soul.

Two natures meet on the human plane and are focalized in Man. These are the animal ego, and the higher self; the one, an inheritance from lower life, the other an overshadowing from the next higher plane.

The animal principle is selfishness; the divine principle is altruism.

However defective in other respects human nature may be, all human endeavor must finally be measured by the principle of altruism, and must stand or fall by the measure in which it inspires and uplifts humanity.

Literary criticism, however justifiable and however valuable, is not the highest tribunal; were it so, the following pages would never have seen the light. The highest tribunal is the criterion of truth, and the test of truth is by its use and beneficence.

Superstition is not religion; speculation is not philosophy; materialism is not science; but true religion, true philosophy, and true science are ever the handmaids of truth.

The study of man by himself should, first of all, point out the possibility of improvement, and so far as possible suggest the methods and indicate the means by which improvement may be realized. This is the motive which has brought out this work, and no one can be more sensible of its many defects than its author. If, however, this book should encourage an abler pen to more competent endeavor in the same direction, the most sanguine expectations of its author will have been realized.

The writer's most sincere acknowledgments are due to his friend and co-laborer, Dr. J. M. Crawford, whose ripe scholarship, now so widely recognized in his translation of the Kalevala, has greatly improved these pages. The conscientiousness with which he has sought to preserve the exact meaning of the author, while critically reviewing these pages, is as creditable as his scholarship is commendable.

With this introduction, this book is given to the reader in the hope that it may encourage and uplift, though it be but a little, that great orphan, Humanity.

J. D. B.

Cincinnati, O., November 20, 1888.

TABLE OF CONTENTS.

(xix)

CHAPTER VII.

The cosmic form a universal duality: male and female:
Adam Cadman: involution and evolution: every form
in nature is a duality: every perfect unity a harmonious duality: cosmos evolved out of chaos: ideal forms
evolved from earthly shapes: spirit broods over matter:
nature builds by law through pure mathematics: man
is taught by suffering, and suffers that he may teach:
creeds and fossils: man the epitome of all: the human
embryo and the law of development: community of
function in lower forms: differentiation in higher
forms the principle of development: the cerebral lobes:
how they are to be regarded: evolution alone insufficient: life tendency diffused throughout all matter: all
lower forms of life are fragments of the human: the
higher animals rudimentary human beings: inheritance
and environment: the ideal form an overshadowing
presence: selfishness and charity: egotism and altruism:
tissue, cell, germ, ovum, fertilization: the process of
reproduction: aggregation and segregation: the origin
of form: fertilization a double process the positing
of a center of life and the unfolding of a still interior

CHAPTER VIII.

Magnetism and life: the life principle pervades all matter: differentiation and the ebb and flow of life: no fast
lines between living and non-living matter: successive planes of life from lowest to highest: vain efforts to
discover the missing links in the chain of human forms:
one plane of life overlaps or overshadows another:
every human personality is a composite body: man's
relation to all surrounding life: the meaning of man's
birthright: the predominance of one plane: physical,
vital, sensuous, intellectual and spiritual personalities:
the animal in rags and the animal in broadcloth:
human tigers and hyenas: every individual possesses a
definite amount of energy: gymnastic exercise and

CHAPTER XI.

A STUDY OF MAN.

CHAPTER I.

THE CRITERION OF TRUTH.

Personality is the most patent fact, and the most potent factor in the life of man; it tinges all he touches, and is the colored glass through which he views the world. The average individual finds it exceedingly difficult, if not impossible, to avoid an inherent tendency to convert all problems that present themselves in thought or life into terms of self-interest. So true is this principle, and so general its operation, that it is exceedingly doubtful if any word in any langauge conveys precisely the same meaning to any two persons; hence arise the misuse and misinterpretation of words as the most prolific source of the disagreements of men. Both candor and charity compel the affirmation, that truth, in its larger sense, has suffered more from those who have misconceived and misinterpreted it, than from those who have knowingly or willfully opposed it.

For the great majority of mankind the sole criterion of truth is traditional authority. Not only does this hold in matters of religion, codes of ethics, and civil rights, but the whole tenor of individual life is determined by birth and geographical location. So also in matters of science, the authority of a great name is considered sufficient evidence for most persons who cultivate this department of knowledge; while only a small minority undertake to examine the evidence on which a verdict in any case is supposed to have been based. It thus transpires that in most departments of human thought and human endeavor, a few individuals virtually do the thinking for the masses, and by appealing to the prejudices and self-interests of the many, they are enabled to hold in check another minority over whom traditional authority has but slight control; and even where the traditional *dictum* is taken with some grains of allowance, it is still considered as accepted unless openly repudiated. The great majority of people adhere to the religious forms into which they happened to be born, and upon the truth or falsity of which they have not been called upon to pronounce. By education these matters have been so thoroughly ingrained, and so much pains has been taken to render their hold binding and lasting, that it is really strange that any are able to throw off the yoke of authority. Either fortunately or unfortunately, the number of those who are able to break away from traditional authority has very largely increased within the past few decades, while within traditional lines there is everywhere a questioning of authorities, a murmur of discontent presaging a warring of elements in the atmosphere of religious belief.

So-called religious truth a century or two ago assumed jurisdiction even over secular matters, and finally relinquished to science, though with great reluctance, the domain of physics and cosmogony, but only on condition of receiving absolute authority in its own realm. In this age religious truth and scientific truth are one, and that the highest and most important of human knowledge and human interest. In short, the element of progress of to-day, pushed on by the spirit of investigation, has entered every realm of knowledge, and subjected it to searching investigation. One of the inevitable results of all this questioning has been to suggest to the less thoughtful that nothing sacred in any realm remains. A little deeper thought will show that nothing in the way of real knowledge can be regarded as unclean or secular; it will show that all truth is given by inspiration, and that every true revelation of nature is a divine revelation to man. The reason for all these changes is not far to seek. The element of man's personality already mentioned, and which colors all he touches, lies at the root of these changes in individual belief and public sentiment. The battle at this point has been a severe one; and the issues are not even yet decided, though they are in no way uncertain. In the ebb and flow of generation after generation, ancient records and sacred traditions have been so modified by special pleading, and so incorporated with human interest, that thousands of honest seekers after truth have been sacrificed under the cloak of authority because they dared to question the prevailing interpretation of these writings. It is a matter of history that Michael Servetus, the earlier discoverer of the circulation of the blood, and one of the brightest minds of the age in which he lived, was burned to death in a slow fire of green wood, not because he denied or disbelieved the Bible, nor was in any way lacking in religious devotion, but because he dared to take issue with an ignorant, arrogant and vindictive priest in power, who intimidated his fellow-priests to help execute his revenge on a brother who had the better of him in an argument. If so-called Divine revelation were everywhere explicit, thus requiring no interpreters, and appealing directly to the conscience and understanding of man, it would be at once shorn of the element of human weakness and error. That which in any age is meant by the word *orthodox* has little reference to any book or any tradition claimed to be divine, but to certain interpretations which men, weak and ignorant like ourselves, have from time to time put upon such records and traditions. It is high time that this fact should be clearly apprehended by every one who assumes the prerogative of thinking for himself, because the knowledge of this fact will enable him to discriminate, and while questioning, as he has the right to do, the opinions of others, he will not be so ready to deny and repudiate the sacred Word. No department of human endeavor reveals more of the weakness, the ignorance and the arrogance of man, and his propensity to disagree and denounce, than his efforts to interpret the Scriptures. These records have reached us through the infirmities of speech, through the imperfections of human language, and further filtered through the weaknesses of human nature. Through these avenues only has any truth been transmitted from Deity to man.

The parables and symbols of the great religions contain more intrinsic truth, and more co-ordinate harmony than any verbal explanation of man has yet given to the world; and that which, more than all other causes combined, has hitherto prevented these grand truths from reaching the masses, is the conceit and arrogance with which ignorance has clung to her false interpretations, thus making it in former times well-nigh impossible, and in later times exceedingly difficult for the earnest seeker to find the real truth.

Whenever man has attempted to explain the symbols which so largely constitute the sacred records of all religions, without a full comprehension of the truth so symbolized, he has invariably made confusion more confounded. In these later days, when a larger and deeper apprehension of truth in every direction is dawning on the human race, and when freedom to pursue truth into every hiding-place, has brought the conviction that such a pursuit is not only man's highest prerogative, but also his binding duty, there is reason to believe that the truth underlying the outer form of the sacred text is slowly being apprehended. As Carlyle puts it: "All visible things are emblems. What thou seest is not there on its own account; strictly speaking, is not there at all. Matter exists only spiritually, and to represent some idea and body it forth."

What we call the *authority of science* is largely determined by the latest utterances of its most intelligent cultivators. These utterances are generally guarded and usually just, setting forth the weak as well as the strong points of any hypothesis with equal care and conscientiousness. A large majority, however, of so-called scientists overlook these qualifications, and set forth the new theory as a fact, and then quote the masters in science as authority for their statements. Thus we find this burden of authority in one form or another pre-empting the fertile domains of human knowledge, so that it is often more difficult to get rid of the old squatter with his false title than it is to locate and record the newcomer with his fee-simple.

It may thus be seen that the approaches to knowledge are seriously obstructed by zeal and self-interest; and that great fortitude is necessary to scale the foothills, before beginning to ascend the delectable mountains of truth.

So far as the evidence of truth is based on human authority, that evidence is, therefore, always open to criticism; and the truth itself, no matter where it may be found and by whatsoever name it may be designated, is a legitimate subject for study and reinvestigation. Truth in one department of knowledge is as divine as in any other, when it is once seen that it is the truth alone that is sacred, and not the departments man has erected, nor the barriers he has laid across her pathway. Every sincere seeker for the simple truth, therefore, carries with him his patent to investigate for himself; this patent being a part of his direct inheritance from his Creator. He must not forget, however, that this unalienable right has coupled with it the duty of honest service, and that this service is to follow every sincere conviction. It is an old doctrine of the church that the repudiation of authority incurs grave responsibility. He who would shirk the responsibility is in no wise worthy of the freedom to think and act for himself, nor will he long enjoy such freedom, for the bondage of fear is always the handmaid of superstition, and the service of truth can alone make man free.

Human knowledge naturally divides into departments,

as physics and metaphysics, science and art, while the department designated as religion, howsoever mixed it may be with superstition, is not generally supposed to bear any relation to other departments of knowledge. As religion is in the province of man, and as it involves a large part of his activities and largely determines his conduct, the sincere truth-seeker will be unable to avoid it if he should so desire, for if his purpose be sincere, his search warrant is absolute.

The various departments of knowledge are often conceived as being at war with each other. The direct inference is, that each being true, truth is therefore at war with itself. Such an inference, however, is absurd; for the most patent sign of falsehood is, always and everywhere, disagreement. Falsehood invariably contradicts itself; truth, never. Therefore, if discrepancies arise between the different departments of knowledge, it places thereby suspicion on all; but it must be remembered that this suspicion rests solely on the human side of the equation, and in no sense pertains to truth itself. The personal lens of colored glass may make truth appear to one red and to another blue, like the two sides of the shield in the old fable; but this can only be the pure white light of truth separated into its component colors by the personal lens. But if every individual is to use his own lens, as indeed he must, he should also remember that his is but one of many colors, and that the tints and shades due to combinations are practically limitless. If he will also bear in mind that truth itself is both tintless and taintless, he will never insist that his own is the one true color.

It may easily be seen that many of the expressions in common use not only arise from misapprehension and inadvertency, but that they are necessarily and directly the cause of error. The terms *scientific truth, philosophic truth, religious truth,* would seem to imply that truth in one of these departments differs from truth in another. It will presently be shown that not only is truth itself hereby misapprehended, but that these very departments are by no means comprehended. Our investigations, therefore, might begin with the inquiry, What is philosophy? What is science? What is religion? before we inquire, What is truth?

One of the most popular errors of the day is the somewhat notorious use of the term "Christian science," in a manner that reveals great ignorance of both terms thus employed. The inference is that Christian science is something entirely different from any other science. If arrogance in statement, if contention and strife for priority in promulgation, and if exorbitant fees and concealment of so-called truth be essentially *Christian,* then the Sermon on the Mount must be un-Christian. Not only has enough of these costly secrets leaked out to show that not a single new secret is therein contained, but that far more and better can be had elsewhere for the asking. The only new thing is the fencing this old subject in with a new name for purposes of exorbitant revenue, to be derived by imposing on the ignorant and credulous. Many of the principles contained are undeniably true, and many of its cultivators are people of high life and unblemished character. Like so many other cases, however, known to all history, they are better than their creed. Arrogance, avarice, and strife, even when found under the sacred name of truth, lead inevitably to but one destiny: confusion and desolation.

All scientific testimony is said by Huxley to depend on "valid evidence, and sound reasoning." While the rules of logic are now so well defined that among educated people there will be little disagreement as to what constitutes "sound reasoning," different scholars will differ necessarily as to what constitutes "valid evidence." Such, however, is one of the latest utterances of physical science, put forth by one of its foremost cultivators, a man as competent to judge of evidence in the domain he specially cultivates as any man living. It must be seen, if his definition of what constitutes scientific evidence is to be universally accepted, that instead of laying the foundation for real evidence and becoming a criterion of truth, it can only stand in the service of authority, or disappear at the first encounter of rival factions in his own beloved field. Huxley's whole life, however, has been one pronounced and dignified protest against this very giant, authority. Let us not forget that falsity always and everywhere not only contradicts itself, but contradicts truth as well; while truth contradicts falsity, but always, and everywhere, it agrees with itself. Not only must every fact in physics agree with every other fact; every theorem of metaphysics be capable of reconciliation with every other theorem; and every truth in religion agree with every other truth; but every fact, theorem, and truth in all the departments of universal knowledge must agree from beginning to end. No human mind has ever been able to determine and to comprehend this universal reconciliation. Such a mind would be able to comprehend and formulate *absolute* truth. Every searcher for truth who realizes that he has not reached the goal where all seeking ends in absolute knowing, may, nevertheless, realize that these conditions and relations belong to truth, the essence of which he does not comprehend. He may thence deduce the proposition: that the apprehension of knowledge consists quite as much in removing discrepancies, and irreconcilable paradoxes, as in the study of truths clearly demonstrated. Any knowledge that man may acquire can come to him only through his own personal investigations. He might as well expect his body to be nourished by the food that another has eaten as to expect his mind to be cultured by another's thoughts or experiences. Blind intellectual belief—a sort of self-delusion— may possibly be thus derived; but true knowledge and true faith, never. The basis of all knowledge is experience. The test of all knowledge is use. In the pursuit and attainment of knowledge two processes, sensation and reason, are always combined, whether consciously or unconsciously. These processes concern "valid evidence and sound reasoning," but these are processes in the acquirement of evidence, not in the evidence itself. These pertain solely to the mind that investigates truth; while truth itself is entirely another matter. For instance, our senses tell us that a certain thing is hot, but they do not tell us what heat is. In this way we learn only our relations to heat, and its effect upon us. To a fabled race of salamanders, or to a man clothed in asbestos, heat appears to be a very different thing indeed; yet in this case it has not changed its essential character. Furthermore, so simple a sensation as that of heat is under no circumstances experienced in the same degree by any two individuals.

By "valid evidence" is undoubtedly meant evidence of the senses; and while under certain general conditions there is, no doubt, universal agreement, this criterion can only approximate or lead up to real evidence; and that, too, only from the physical point of view. In all that pertains to objective phenomena, evidence is derived through the senses by analysis and by experiment; and the validity of such testimony is determined by repetition, by corroboration, and by sound reasoning. We have evidence of the senses approved and confirmed by reason, and human methods weighed by human judgment. The mind, which is here said to reason on the evidence of the senses, is supposed to be the result of physical development, the so-called function of the brain. Here the thing examined, the senses by which it is examined, and the mind by which the evidence is weighed and measured, are all of the same general character, viz., phenomenal. The natural manifestation, the evidence, and the judgment depend upon motion. Consciousness as a fact, and as a factor, is either virtually left out of the question, or in the dilemma to which its admission as a factor gives rise is classed with mind, and put in the same category with the results of physical evolution. The difficulty to which such action leads can not be either ignored or explained away. It results in the forced explanation of subjective

experience in terms of objective phenomena, and eventually
to the practical elimination of the subjective factor. If
such a result were true and found adequate to cover all human experiences, nothing could be said against it and everything for it. We can never solve an equation by dealing
only with one of its members, and the cosmic or human equation is no exception. Whenever a really thoughtful and intelligent person is willing to be written down an out-and-out
materialist, it is evidence that he is vainly trying to solve the
equation of life by dealing only with one of its members.
He may still imagine that the methods he employs, and which
lead to unsatisfying results, will, in the future, lead to conclusions more satisfactory. It is part of his nihilism, however, to conclude that no better results are possible to any
one. If he could be led to see that the fault lies solely in
his methods, and that by ignoring one member of his equation he has made logical and faultless solution impossible,
he might undertake to improve his methods. These better
methods may be learned in the growth of a blade of grass,
no less than in the bloom and beauty of the lilies of the field.
The process by which we learn is the one process by which
nature builds. Nature is never at cross-purposes with herself, else she could never have evolved cosmos out of chaos,
nor created the everlasting foundations of truth.

The following suggestions are a mere outline of the factors and conditions involved in this problem.

Take man as we find him. Let us now suppose him to be
divided into two equal parts for a working hypothesis. Let
us call one part the objective, and the other the subjective.
Hence we would have objective and subjective nature; objective and subjective man. Let us consider analogy the
bridge, or process, whereby, in our investigations, we may
pass from one condition to the other. Let us call matter
and spirit the two poles of one substance. The theater for
the display of matter is then the material, the physical, the
phenomenal, the objective, or the natural world. The

theater for the operation of spirit is the subjective, spiritual, or *noumenal* world. Man being a part of this dual world of matter and spirit, his nature is derived from both. It is of no consequence now in what degree, or in what proportion, for man's equation is not yet solved; at best, it is only in process of solution. Let us further consider consciousness as the central fact in man's being; and let us diagrammatically figure consciousness as a central point between his two conditions—the natural and the spiritual. Let us remember that, while we know nothing of the real essence of consciousness, we may, nevertheless, study it as a fact, and discover its relations to the objective and subjective in man. Let us think of the origin of self-consciousness in man as the very center and quintessence of the germ from which his bodily fabric has been evolved; and that it has grown and expanded with his growth, including the natural and spiritual nature, adjusting itself to all conditions and relations of structure and function within and without. Let us further consider the growth and development of the germ and all its subsequent unfolding in the life of man, as an evolution of form and faculty on the outer physical plane; and, again, as an involution of essence and type from the spiritual or subjective plane—consciousness expanding as the body expands and as function unfolds, but always maintaining the same relations to structure and function, and always seeking equilibrium in the eccentric and concentric life of man.

We have here a logical and wholly consecutive unfolding of human life on the two planes of existence first predicated. We have these three factors concerned in all processes of thinking or knowing, viz., objective being, consciousness and subjective being. It is generally agreed that experience is the basis and the condition of all knowing. Experience, then, may pertain largely to either side of the equation, though it can entirely ignore neither; for to disregard one member is to annul the foundation and conditions of life

itself. Now let us conceive that life consists in the translation of the two worlds, the natural, and the spiritual, into
terms of consciousness, through experience of both; and
that the brain-pictures, or all strictly mental operations, consist of the combined experiences derived from these two
sources, reflected back upon the super-sensitive cerebral con-
volutions, and thus constituting man's intellectual world—
his personal kingdom created through his individual experiences. We then see the depth of meaning in the verse:

> "My mind to me a kingdom is."

This concept renders a spiritual thinkable as the counterpart and complement of the natural. There is far more in
support of this universal equation than at first appears. The
physical world thus becomes but the embodiment and manifestation of the spiritual, in terms of matter, space, time and
motion. In other words, it becomes the concentration of the
ideal, the spiritual; and the spiritual becomes the natural
idealized or perfected. True progress for man is a straight-
forward climbing, on the rundles of experience, up the lad-
der of light, from a lower to a higher being; while retro-
gression is a journeying in the opposite direction, and leads
to disolution and destruction.

Something akin to this conception must have been in the
mind of Thomas Carlyle when he wrote: "Matter exists only
spiritually, and to represent some idea and body it forth."

If to experience is to know, then to know is to become.
To know the truth is to become the truth. Hence the evidence of the senses is partial testimony derived only from
one side of being; and, no matter how logically such evidence may be used in reasoning, so long as it is unsupple-
mented by evidence reaching consciousness from the other
side of man's being, it may lead to opinions, and be assigned
a place in the intellectual kingdom of man; but it can play
no part in the everlasting kingdom of truth. Science and

philosophy are in no sense formulated results, but simply methods, when rightly apprehended and correctly used. Neither process alone can ever arrive at absolute truth. Science may discover facts; philosophy may disclose principles; and the co-operation of both, as methods, may aid the understanding of man in the apprehension of truth. Hence the expressions *scientific* truth, *philosophic* truth, and *metaphysic* truth, are misnomers. All science is philosophic; all philosophy is scientific; and all true religion is scientific, philosophic and metaphysic. Both science and philosophy are religious, so far as the natural province of one touches upon or overlaps the other; for each is but a method whereby the consciousness of man, which is *one,* seeks truth, which is also *one.* The criterion of truth for man lies not in the estimate of the senses, nor in a specific process of reasoning upon phenomena confined to one-half of his nature; but in the co-ordinate harmony which he is able to bring out of the chaos of all his varied experiences. The disharmony and jarring discord belong to man; the harmony and pleasing concord, in all their fullness of beauty, belong to truth; and when all discord disappears, and universal concord appears, then truth will belong to man. Then, and then only, will man and truth be one. To know is to live the truth.

CHAPTER II.

MATTER AND FORCE.

Though scientists have hitherto been unable to agree as to the essential nature and constitution of matter, and though they confess their entire ignorance of the essence of force, yet no one who has given the subject any serious consideration will for a moment doubt that matter, in some form, has always existed. Certain writers may attach arbitrary meanings to such expressions as *primordial atoms,* and claim for science itself that certainty and exactness for which it everywhere seeks credence. It is well to remember that, on many occasions, the foremost advocates of science have confessed their entire ignorance of the final constitution of things; and that, at best, they only entertain hypotheses, in support of which they have only probabilities to urge. Even these may disappear tomorrow in the light of some larger discovery. The highways of knowledge are everywhere strewn with the wrecks of old hypotheses, though many of the fragments may still be recognized in the newer structures that have replaced them. Thus the vortices of Descartes appear in latest theories as the inter-molecular spaces or dynaspheres; and the monads of Leibnitz are largely tributary to our idea of atoms and molecules. In chemistry, many of the old ideas may still be recognized in their new dress, and in spite of an entirely new nomenclature.

The test of a theory is its application to fact, and to the sequence of its relations to other facts and theories. No theory, applicable to very wide groups of facts, is ever quite satisfactory in all cases. Whenever it very nearly approaches this condition, the theory gives place to a recognized law of nature. The student of nature thus carefully feels his way, step by step, from theory to fact; from hypothesis to law; while the most certain knowledge possessed by science, regarding the ultimate structure of things, is the certainty that it does not know. The atomic theory, now so generally in vogue, offers no exception to the above reflections. If, therefore, science is thus uncertain with regard to matter and force, no theory can be called orthodox; and any suggested modification of any theory is legitimate.

Very important discoveries have been made in recent times, but these discoveries concern the relations, rather than the essence of things. The finer appliances of modern art in mechanics and physics, together with the higher unfolding of the senses in man, have brought to view large groups of facts in nature's finer forces; while the records of all these discoveries are so widely diffused, that relations are also discovered between different groups of facts that at first seemed entirely dissimilar.

The mechanical equivalence of heat with correlative modes of motion, as now apprehended, and the general principle of the correlation of force, to which the former discovery gave rise, led also to the concept of the conservation or indestructibility of force. It would fill volumes to record the advancement in physical science that has followed these great discoveries.

Among the more recent deductions in the realm of the higher dynamics are two discoveries which, from a scientific point of view, not only seem to transcend all others, but seem also to open the door to a new world—not as dissevered from the old world of crude matter and force, but intimately connected with it. These are the discovery of vibratory energy by Mr. Keely, and that of radiant matter by Mr. Crookes. The intrinsic value and wide range of applicability of these two discoveries will be best apprehended by those who are also familiar with the rapid unfolding of the higher sensibility of man, as witnessed by thousands of careful students and experimenters in the realm of psychology. So rapid, indeed, has been the advancement in this last-named direction, and so potent and dangerous the forces and power revealed, that legal enactments have already been instituted to control experiments and protect society against the threatened danger. It may thus readily be seen that progress in physics goes hand in hand with progress in metaphysical discovery. To appreciate the one, it is necessary to keep in view also the other, as together indicating the signs of the times. We are thus beginning to realize the refinement of which matter and force are capable; and the *terra incognita,* whose shores we have thus been permitted to approach, is destined to swallow up not only the unknown but also the hitherto *unknowable* in both these realms.

The methods of modern science are approximately exact; but the results at which it has arrived are by no means final. In the use of the term "exact science," this important fact is not always kept clearly in view. The relative force of any scientific *dictum* being thus clearly defined, it will also appear that all questions, here as elsewhere, are open questions. With every important discovery there is a checking back over all previous conclusions, and the inaccuracies, thus made to disappear, become constantly less and less prominent. A path so often trodden in time becomes smooth.

It is no part of our purpose to cast reproach upon any of the discoveries of science, nor seriously to question the results at which it has arrived, so long as they are thus held tentatively. All scientists, by the way, worthy of the name, thus look upon the results of their investigations. If, in dealing with pure physics, science has achieved final results in nothing, and can really boast only of more or less exact methods of research, then no one wearing the garb of science can afford to ridicule either philosophy, psychology, or religion. Each of these departments can boast of methods quite as exact as those of science itself; for there is a true psychology, as there is a true science. Here again, as will be more fully shown elsewhere, the truth lies in the method and not in the partial results; for inasmuch as the results are, in all cases, tentative or provisional, rather than final, they are not results, but methods.

The idea of the eternity or indestructibility of matter can be traced back to very remote times; and, though the theory of the correlation and conservation of force, in its present form, is of recent date, glimpses of it may be found even beyond our present epoch. Plato says that we see by virtue of the light which is in the eye commingling with that of the sun; thus implying terms of correlation; while in the Sanscrit terms of the still more ancient Hindoo philosophies the principle is more clearly apprehended.

We have, then, the indestructibility of matter, the hypothetical atom, and the indestructibility of force. Matter is the theater of motion, and offers resistance to force, though not in the sense of the old idea of inertia; and force is that which produces motion in matter. The conclusion is, therefore, inevitable: there is no matter without force, and no force without matter. They are indestructible and inseparable. Therefore, every hypothetical atom, as every particle of mass, is in ceaseless motion; for if an atom cease to move, it must cease to be. With every change in the relations and combinations of atoms, new forces, or different modes of motion, are manifested. Even a nascent point in the breaking up of compounds, and in the formation of new ones, cannot be conceived where motion ceases for an instant; this would annihilate force. Motion can only be transformed into other modes, like the change of figures in an endless dance, weaving new forms in the dizzy whirl of life and death.

Certain experiments, notably those of Tyndall on soundwaves, have shown that small particles of matter, like grains of sand, free to move, as on a drumhead, or any vibrating disc, will arrange themselves in exact geometrical figures, according to the sound-wave directly or indirectly induced. In the transmission of motion from without, through waves of air, there is a visible response from the free-moving molecules, as when the disc is also made to vibrate directly; in either case, geometrical figures are produced. The principle of consonant rhythm is illustrated by the tuning of two pianos in unison, and witnessing in one instrument the repetition of tones or chords produced on the other. A large class of substances in nature are recognized by the form and color of the crystals to which they give rise. The requisite condition for crystallization is solution, so that the particles of the crystallizing substances shall be free to move among themselves; without solution the process is a very slow one. This movement of particles to produce exact forms is crudely illustrated by the sand-grains. The uniform shape of the crystals formed by any given substance shows that substance to be capable of responding to certain definite waves of motion only; and it shows, also, that the form of the wave here underlies, rather than impinges upon, the crystallizing substance, polarizing it, as we shall see further on. Within and without, however, there must be consonant rhythm; and the form of the crystals, as doubtless to some extent their color and prismatic quality, are determined by the equilibrium established between the external and internal waves of motion. This adjustment of motions must be by exact ratios, or equimultiples, according to the principles of harmony. It is by no means, then, a fanciful conclusion, from the foregoing outlines, that every atom of matter in the universe is set to music, and that the forms of crystals, and all the varied shapes in nature, lie concealed in rhythm and laws of harmony. The very atoms may be said to sing for joy in the dawn of every created form; for life is essential harmony, and harmony is joy.

In the formation of all chemical compounds there may be traced certain definite laws of proportion that one substance bears to another; and though one or more substances may, singly or together, enter into many compounds, the proportions and relations are, in every case, predetermined and arbitrarily fixed. No matter what artificial compounds man may discover or devise, he can only conform to this fixed and inherent law of proportion; if he strives to ignore it, nature only laughs at his folly and conceit, and stubbornly refuses to combine in any other way. A very important part of chemistry consists in the discovery of inherent laws of proportion.

We thus discern not only force, but principles, underlying all phenomena of nature. The process of crystallization shows the persistence of an underlying force everywhere present, and operating in a uniform manner. This force must be judged by its effects. We know far less of its own mode of motion than of the mode which it induces in matter. It is quite conceivable that the various modes of motion, designated as heat, light, electricity, and the like, are but modifications of this one underlying force, or its phenomenal display under varying conditions of vibration. Thus are determined the phenomena of organization no less than those of crystallization. This idea of a widely diffused and basic force implies also a basic substance with which it is inseparably connected; else must we change our previous concepts of matter and force.

Creative energy displays an apparent or relative fixation of forms in the midst of unceasing change. Organization, like crystallization, is, in a crude sense, a temporary fixation of form. The first step in this fixation of form is polarization. Diffused and indefinite waves or vibrations concentrate and become definite, and follow given lines. We have seen that this polarizing tendency subtends all phenomena, and all building up of forms in inorganic nature. The same principle will be shown to obtain in morphology, or in organic nature. There is, in every sense, a change from the formless to the formed, and the more definite the form the greater its stability.

If we consider the so-called elementary substances, such as science has hitherto been unable to analyze, as made up of invisible atoms, similar atoms being grouped to form an element, with certain definite relations existing between different groups, we shall be justified in supposing that all of the so-called elements have something in common. Hence, from the matter-side of our ploblem, as from the force-side, we can think back to a common *substratum*. If from the force-side we discern a polarizing tendency, and from the matter-side a substratum, our superstructure, which we found uniting at the apex as matter and force, must be even more compact at its base. We thus discern an underlying substance everywhere diffused, of great tenuity, permeating all things, as the common basis of matter and force. This substance, with its characteristic polarizing tendency, and its universal diffusibility, outwardly displayed in atoms of elements, and in all objective phenomenal nature, is magnetism. If magnetism be also atomic in structure, the atoms may be conceived as infinitely smaller than those of the elements; and as this *substratum* may be considered as either matter or force, lying back of both, it answers to the dynaspheric force, which at once unites and separates, holds together, and yet keeps apart, the larger atoms of the various forms of matter designated as solid, fluid and gas. The so-called "radiant matter" would be magnetism itself, divorced from all other matter, freed from the so-called elements, radiant when not beclouded by overlying grosser atoms, yet matter still. If this view, thus far, is warranted by such facts as we possess, we must go still farther back in our analysis. That which underlies both matter and force, and thus surrounds both molecule and mass, and which is recognized in all matter as a polarizing tendency, yet only a finer grade of matter, must, therefore, lie at the center of, as well as diffuse our hypothetical atoms, and so polarize them. Aggregations of atoms to form elements, and aggregations of elements to form compounds, as well as aggregations to form crystals and organisms, can be logically conceived as polarizations. Elements may thus be positive, and others negative as to each other, and so give rise to the locking of atoms to form compounds. The atoms of substances like oxygen may have complex poles; while others like hydrogen may have simple poles. Hence many forms of attraction would rise from polarization. If magnetism itself is simply luminous, and this luminous substance stands potentially for what we call matter and force, the motion which here, as elsewhere, is the logical sequence, can be conceived as a quivering or exceedingly rapid vibration, an infinite number of infinitesimal atoms within an invisible area, vibrating with incalculable rapidity. Groups of such atoms by transference of this vibration into scintillations would appear luminous; or if motion were transformed into waves in a definite direction in matter, they would polarize it; or in rarefied matter, would give rise to light; or again in more solid matter, to heat; and so on with the round of physical forces.

We are still in the realm of matter and force, or phenomenal nature, and we may still go back of all this and dig deeper. It must not be forgotten that with every change in the mode of motion, or correlation of force, there is induced a corresponding change in the so-called properties of matter. If the different forces arise from the one force, magnetism, so must the different elements arise from the one substance, magnetism. Thus we may conceive of all attractions or affinities. We have so far reasoned back to the common basis of visible nature displayed as matter and force. Magnetism would seem to be the matrix of matter, and the parent of force. This view is immensely fortified, at every step, by the phenomena and sensations of animal magnetism, or hypnotism.

The theater in which are displayed the phenomena of matter and force we call space; but, unless we are very guarded, our concept of atoms will lead us to an absurd concept of space. Having traced our atoms to minuteness sufficient for our purposes, and having relinquished the idea of dimension regarding them, dimension thus merging in immensity, space remains as mere emptiness—a boundless vacuum, in which the finer atoms float. This, however, is altogether inconsistent with the eternity of matter and force in any form, as this would involve the idea of both the beginning and the end of matter and force—the equivalent of saying that there was a time when there was absolutely nothing. Time cannot antedate phenomena, for it belongs to the succession of phenomena; and it is inconceivable apart from motion. What then is space, as logically related to other concepts? In beginning, let us change names, and so get rid of the dangerous idea of emptiness. For space let us say ether, not ether in space, but ether as space itself. Let us think of this ether as boundless, continuous, therefore unparticled, and thus without qualities or attributes, as we apprehend them on the physical side. While forming the *substratum* for magnetism, as magnetism forms the *substratum* for matter and force, outwardly ether will be the boundary between the objective and the subjective worlds. If we think of the natural world as adhering to the ether and displayed outwardly, we may think of the spiritual world as also adhering to the same ether but displayed inwardly. If the sensuous life of man is related to the phenomena of outer nature displayed by atoms of matter and modes of motion, so is the supersensuous life of man related to subjective nature displayed with basic continuity and essential form, with consciousness as the middle term equally related to both worlds—the objective, atomic world of matter, and the subjective, continuous world of spirit. Thus, in atoms and suns, in the infinitely small as in the infinitely great, in center and circumference, the natural and the spiritual are still *one*. If by analogy we seek to penetrate beyond the ether, we must either abandon our idea of atoms, or conceive of matter now in its upward ascent approaching its opposite pole, spirit, as also existing in another state. But we can abandon here our atomic hypothesis without abandoning matter itself. The continuity of matter refined beyond the purest ether is thinkable, and our concept of spirit thus becomes as rational as our concept of matter, seeing that we know the essential nature of neither, and can only partially comprehend relations. The basis of the continuity on the one side, and the basis of the atoms on the other, is the ether. As on the physical side, mass and so-called inertia, or gross matter, appears to predominate, so on the spiritual side, force appears to predominate and matter seems to be held in abeyance. This shifting of factors would constitute for us the natural and the spiritual world—our idea of the universe. In thus exchanging the idea of vacuity for that of continuity, we do no violence to any rational concept of matter and force. It will be no longer rational to talk about vacuum or partial vacuum. We can well afford to dispense with the term, since it has ceased to convey any rational idea.

If our reasoning thus far holds and magnetism be found to be the fourth state of matter, ether would seem to be a fifth; and the series would stand thus: solid, liquid, gas, magnetism, ether. With this conclusion, we shall have both to modify and to enlarge our idea of atoms and elementary substances. In the case of that of the most active and most widely diffused element, oxygen, for example, we may conceive of one of its atoms as consisting of concentrated rings or layers, a ring of magnetism enclosed in an outer capsule and inclosing an inner nucleus of ether with each of these rings or spheres penetrating the others, the mere gross being aggregations or concentrations of the more refined. We may further conceive of vibrations intense enough and rapid enough to disassociate the outer rings from the ether, though unable to liberate pure force, yet competent to bring into activity in another form far more refined and intense the substance, magnetism, which is both matter and force; and this Mr. Keely seems to have accomplished. Something like this occurs when water is decomposed by a current of electricity. If it be once conceived that substances akin to oxygen, called elements, have originated from magnetic substance, it may also be seen how they may return to their primordial matrix. Ozone may thus be found to be an intermediate state between oxygen and magnetism; one form may be polarized oxygen, and the other non-polarized This idea of the compound nature of atoms is not new, nor is it without support. The magnetism of an iron bar may be explained by assuming that the atoms that compose it are polarized, the property of the bar representing the qualities of the atoms combined. In all germs from which living forms arise the structure is similar to that suggested for an atom of oxygen. Reasoning backward by analogy, as in the case of the magnetic bar, there must either be a break at some point in the orderly sequence of nature, or every atom that goes to form the germ must typically represent it.

Matter and force, inseparable and indestructible, may, nevertheless, disappear from view; they may pass from the active to the passive plane and still exist as invisible, unparticled matter and potential force. This view is also supported by analogy. Every process visible to man consists in a crude sense of an appearance and a disappearance, of growth and decay, of building up and tearing down, of death and rejuvenescence. The invisible becomes visible; the visible becomes invisible. In this concept we have only traced the process further back, just as we trace the principle of the subdivision of matter back to the concept of invisible atoms. While the quantity of matter and force in the universe may be conceived as forever the same, unceasing motion leads creative processes out from the bosom of the all-enfolding ether only to lead them back to the source from whence they came, and so constitute and continue the cycles of creation. Here, again, analogy supports our argument. If suns and planets revolve, they must have de-

rived the forces by which they revolve from some principle antedating their appearance, viz., the cyclic process of
creation itself.

If the foregoing considerations seem transcendental, let
it be remembered that we are presently to enter the realm
of vital dynamics, there to examine the processes of life
and of thought. We shall find these processes complicated,
though made up of the display of matter and force, the same
matter and the same force that are herein discussed. There
can be no essential difference between matter and force
found in the living structure and that found outside of it;
otherwise the latter could not be converted into the former.
Nutrition brings about such a conversion. It may thus be
seen, that to begin the study of life without at least an outline of the principles of physics, would be as fruitless as to
attempt to solve the most difficult problem of differential
calculus without a knowledge of the laws of differentiation.
The useless theories regarding human nature and human
life arise through ignorance or disregard of these basic
principles. Like plants that grow in the air they take no
root, and flourish only for a brief season.

CHAPTER III.

In the preceding chapter an outline is given of the general principles of physics, as pertaining particularly to matter and force, in their basic relations and manifestations in smaller areas. We are now briefly to consider those wider displays regarding nature as a whole. If man derives his body and his energy from matter and force it follows that he is also a part of the world about him, an existence in space and time. To a certain extent he is related to all nature. If we would clearly discern at what point and to what extent man transcends the sphere of physics, we must first definitely determine his relations to that sphere.

The persistence of motion as coincident with matter and force implies ceaseless change. This change involves atom, particle, molecule and mass. It therefore involves all organisms, whether animal, vegetable or mineral. Instability and transition are indelibly stamped on all created things. Nothing is what it seems, as all things exist only by virtue o1 change, ceaseless change. All human experience, which is the basis of all our knowledge, is a record of changes occurring in our states of consciousness.

Creation naturally divides into halves matter and spirit. Spirit transcends matter as refinement transcends grossness, as light transcends darkness, as good transcends evil. Matter exists externally as body; spirit, internally as essence. If matter and spirit are the opposite poles of cosmos so are they the opposite poles of an atom, as an atom typifies a universe. A universe made up of particles without affini-

(54)

ties, with no common basis upon which to combine, would not even be conceivable as chaos; it would be a condition unthinkable. There is no more marvelous revelation in nature than the intimate relations everywhere seen. Atoms and molecules flock together like doves seeking their mates. A volume might be written on the Loves of the Atoms, as the elder Darwin, and Ovid before him, wrote on the Loves of the Plants. There could be no attraction, no affinity without duality. This principle is equally true in atoms and in man. Emerson says: "Husband and wife must be very two before they can be very one." If attraction is universal, so is duality. There can be no attraction without something to attract and something to be attracted. Attraction implies both the opposite and the similar; or, more accurately, attraction implies repulsion. These are related to each other as positive and negative poles; hence opposites attract and repel. Attraction and repulsion are either two equal forces, or opposite poles of one force. As motive powers they are equal. Just as one body moves toward another by attraction, it moves from it by repulsion. Two atoms attracted to each other, locked in a firm embrace, saturate each other and become homogeneous. Repulsion separates them just as attraction brought them together. Spirit thus impregnates matter, while matter embodies spirit; and thus are created atoms and worlds. The atomic stability of elementary substances, and the comparative instability of compounds, may thus turn on this problem of impregnation and repulsion. Duality is then both basic and cosmic. One principle leads forth the busy atoms and swings in space the teeming worlds. Our forms of thought and modes of expression not only reveal duality, but both thought and expression originate from duality and are possible only as such. So-called evidence of the senses concerns the external world of phenomena, though beyond the five senses recognized there are others that undoubtedly go deeper and penetrate beyond the objective plane. The senses by which we apprehend the world of phenomena around us are also phenomenal in character; change within, as change without. To sense a thing is to appreciate the changes that characterize it, and the relations that concern it; but to sense only is not to understand, as will be shown further on. All phenomena occur in matter, space, time and motion. In the preceding chapter space was conceived as the underlying ether. In the larger display of nature as related to movements of mass occurring in time, our ideas of space regard distance and dimension; the magnitude of objects and the distance between them, or our ideas of height, depth and breadth, are conditioned by the senses. The eye is thus our space-organ, and the ear our time-organ; while beyond the phenomenal character of external nature and sensation there is also the element of imperfection in the organs of sense. Our ideas of space and time are always relative, never absolute; and are furthermore often defective, owing to defects in us. If one were to imagine himself suspended in space, out of sight of any object upon which the eye could rest, his ideas of distance and of size would soon disappear; and there would also disappear his idea of time. In place of these ideas would come the feeling of immensity. It may thus be seen that our ideas of space and time are definitely related to matter and motion, and that our sensations and thoughts dependent on these are phenomenal also, and are of the same general character. Taking now this objective, phenomenal world as a whole, we find, according to our previous conception, that it constitutes one-half of our knowable world, bodied forth from the ether as the senses are bodied forth from consciousness. Sir Isaac Newton designated the ether *Sensorium Dei;* we might call it the Consciousness of Nature. Thus the sensorium of God is the consciousness of nature; while the consciousness of God is the creator of the world. Thus the Infinite center, the Divine Consciousness, is impressed on the sensitive ether and bodied forth in all created forms; while the same outward nature, through the sensorium and varied experiences of man, is reproduced in his consciousness. Eventually through the unfolding of higher senses the subjective world may be re-created in man. It has elsewhere been suggested that when matter disappears from the visible world beyond the gaseous and below the plane of magnetism, thus becoming unparticled and no longer manifesting as matter and force, as we understand them, motion must also disappear. Matter and force in this hypothesis have changed places and are differently related. To this inner realm elsewhere displayed, as the outer realm is displayed in space and time, we may attach the idea of stability, and there may be as many invisible worlds for the display of this subjective mode of being as there are visible worlds in the objective. It would be reasonable to suppose that every visible world has its invisible counterpart; that there are twin worlds of matter and spirit, as twin atoms, negative and positive—one modulus running through cosmos. We are not at present concerned with these invisible worlds further than to show a logical basis for the concept that the objective world of matter as a whole, as in every part, is supplemented by a subjective world of rest, where the phenomenal becomes the *noumenal*. Thus is carried out our idea of duality, the ether being the common medium of exchange. This subjective world stands related to the objective as cause to effect; and when the resulting cycle of change has run its course there is a return to the subjective world. Here the terms cause and effect change places, and on the subjective plane are worked out the effects of the previous objective existence. Again the cycle is complete, and again there is an output from the subjective to the objective plane. Novel as may seem the foregoing statements, they are everywhere justified by analogies in nature, and are put forth as the logical sequence of the universal principle of polarity, which again rests on cosmic duality, the modulus of nature.

Though the principle of polarity is everywhere manifest, and though it is a clue to the labyrinth of life, to the process of thought and to the destiny of man, its most valuable service is in enabling us to determine the true position and relations of consciousness, thus making rational and comprehensible the process of knowing through experience. Here again involution and evolution, as general expressions for the dual process, conform to the general equation of nature. Very few human equations are complete. Few persons have an equal experience of both objective and subjective nature, and few are really aware how largely experience is involved from the subjective plane. The cosmic duality of which we form a part is so intimately blended with our daily life that it is often entirely overlooked, and is only discerned when we endeavor to discover the real nature of things. So mixed and blended are the varied experiences of life, so complicated all mental processes, that it is difficult to separate any single experience from its fellows in order to discover its basis and meaning. It is true that we can hardly imagine any two experiences as occurring at the same time; but the memory of former experiences and the anticipation of those to come lead inevitably to the very confusion named. With memory on the one side and with hope and fear on the other, past, present and future almost hopelessly bewilder us. It thus transpires that such expressions as *experience, real* and *ideal,* convey no very definite meaning to most persons. All nature is, moreover, full of paradoxes. There are a thousand questions that the thoughtful and sincere can answer in the affirmative or in the negative with equal propriety. This is equivalent to saying that these questions are so involved that they cannot be satisfactorily answered by yea or nay. And it signifies more than this: it signifies that every subject may be viewed from two sides, from the objective, and from the subjective; or from the side of self-interest, and from that of universal interest. These last named are often found to clash. The personal never gives way to the universal without a struggle. Self-preservation is not only the first law of nature, it is the first and the last law, the *alpha* and the *omega* of egotism. Nature everywhere sacrifices individuals to preserve the race. The first, the highest law of nature, is altruism. And it is because man persists in reading this law backwards that humanity suffers and countless millions mourn. Nor is the cup of man's egotism yet full; as egotism enshrines itself in a creed, overleaps the bounds of time, and dooms more than half of the human race to everlasting misery. With the unfolding of the higher faculties of man he will discern a more beneficent purpose in nature; for just in proportion as he rises above self-interest and pride will he truly comprehend the divine. He will find not only that the phenomenal world of sense and time, but that the spiritual world is here and now, and that he has only to open his soul to its divine influence to become conscious of its presence. The key to this unfolding is not self-interest nor egotism, but altruism, whereby the phenomenal and the *noumenal* are made *one* in consciousness and in life.

CHAPTER IV.

PHILOSOPHY AND SCIENCE.

The basis of all knowledge is experience. This has been stated previously and will more fully appear in the sequel. To experience is to know. To learn and to know are not synonymous though they are kindred terms. So far as learning is a mere mental process and related to memory it is to the individual an alien; only as learning enters consciousness and molds the individual life, only as experience thus co-ordinates truth, does learning become real knowledge. For the present we need only say that consciousness bears a different relation to the brain from thought. One learns as he apprehends, and this is a mental process; one knows as he comprehends, and this concerns conscious experience of truth. All knowledge is derived through two factors, the subjective and the objective. Valid evidence and correct reasoning are processes that lead to knowledge, but they are not the only ones. Thinking is that peculiar process of the brain resulting from sensation; it is the experience of sensation. Thought and consciousness are inter-related and mutually dependent in man as now constituted, but they are related as sense and sensorium, as surface and center. Reasoning is thought proceeding in an orderly manner, by which we discern the relations of things. The structure of the brain and its functions exist by virtue of the very principles which by reason we everywhere discover in nature. We might say that these principles have created the brain and mind of man, and that in the very process of knowing man re-creates these principles. If then thought, as a resultant of sensation and feeling, builds the brain, only logical and rational thought can perfect its structure and fully develop its function. Logical thought is the orderly procession of those principles or processes of which reason apprehends the normal relation. Thought like sensation is phenomenal. It depends upon change or motion, and is derived through the senses from the phenomenal world without. Thought is, therefore, the moving panorama of the brain, reproducing the world to consciousness. Evidence of the senses, passed upon by reason and approved by experience, becomes knowledge; but for this knowledge to be in any sense complete, the thing or the principle must have been reproduced in miniature in man. Thus to know a thing is to be the thing known. Thought and feeling, therefore, reproduce the world in consciousness. The thought-pictures are fleeting, but consciousness records and preserves them, not in detail, but in essence as precipitated results. We thus have the thing known, the knower, and the process of knowing. In real knowledge the thing known and the knower are merged into one. Man has become the thing he sought to know, hence the process of knowing disappears; it is consummated. We have seen that knowledge considers facts and relations as they have been transmitted to consciousness by thought and feeling. Facts relate to single things; relations, to one or many things. A fact once determined reveals other relations, and every new relation brings to light other facts. To obtain facts we must tear things apart. To discover relations we must put them together. We obtain facts by analysis. We discover relations by synthesis. These two methods enter, whether consciously or unconsciously, into all our processes of knowing. Science deals more especially with the world of phenomena which includes sensation and thought, leading up to consciousness. The method of science is analysis. Philosophy deals especially with the world of reason, principles and laws, and its method is synthesis; but as both the results of analysis and the results of synthesis combine in consciousness continually, we are seldom able to separate them in consciousness. Reason discovers these two processes of analysis and of synthesis; and as thought presents the world to man, so reason presents man to himself. Man tastes of the world by experience, assimilates it by thought, comprehends it by reason and intuition, and becomes it by consciousness.

Thus it may be seen that philosophy includes and transcends science, as a law of nature transcends a fact, and yet one process cannot dispense with the other, for each has continual need of the other. Each, however, has a field and a method of its own. Science deals with matter in the realm of physics; philosophy, with mind in the realm of metaphysics. As working methods in the process of knowing, science and philosophy cannot be separated, while in the analysis of all processes by reason, even the analysis of reason itself, science and philosophy are separate methods covering different realms, pursued by a single mind to arrive at one truth.

In all our investigations into the nature of man we should seek for valid evidence and employ sound reasoning, if we would arrive at the truth. Observation must go hand in hand with experience, and we may fortify our own experience at every step by the experience of others. In this way we may gain a very wide experience equivalent to our own. Having learned a fact, we do not need to verify it daily. If we taste, it is not essential that we devour; but without experience in some form, or in some degree, it is impossible to know or to become. The value of what we call experience depends entirely on the use we make of it, and the wisdom of the methods by which we obtain it. If experience be our stock in trade from which is derived not only the pleasure of life but the fruit of knowledge, it is also well to remember that what we experience we know, and whatsoever we know we become. Experience and knowledge lead up to being. The *dicta* of science, like the dogmas of religion, are never final. These are to the flight of the soul in pursuit of truth as the sheltering rock is to the weary wings of the eagle, a rest on its journey. The souls of men are weighted down by creeds and dogmas, as though they were final truths. This is like clipping the wings of the eagle and chaining him to the rock. We have already shown that philosophy and science are processes, not results; hence any conclusions arrived at by these processes, whether by deduction or induction, are in no sense final. No result is valid even for a day that is not derived through these two processes combined. The fact derived by inductive analysis of the phenomena in which it is involved must be fortified through synthetic deduction by the world of which it is a part. This involves sufficient evidence and correct reasoning. Man constantly employs the processes which constitute these methods designated as science and philosophy, and the magnitude of the experience does not change the process, nor convert a process into a result. These universal methods lead to similar but not to uniform results; for personal experience, which is everywhere the basis of these methods, varies continually. One who is in any sense a scientist and in no sense a philosopher is by no means a knower. He has facts and opinions rather than knowledge. One who is in any sense a philosopher and in no sense a scientist ignores facts and is a mere speculator. The first is usually a materialist; the second a theorist, and these always cast reproach on both science and philosophy. So also in the name of religion one may be a ritualist, may ignore both science and philosophy, may deny facts, refuse to reason, and so become a servant of superstition. None of these false methods can ever lead to a knowledge of nature, a knowledge of man, or a knowledge of God.

It may thus be seen that a correct apprehension of science and philosophy as methods, and that a correct and intelligent use of these processes lead man to a knowledge of himself, and as this knowledge unfolds through experience it includes all the rest. Man will know God when he becomes God-like.

CHAPTER V.

We behold around us everywhere one all-pervading life. To inquire into the nature and origin of this life is the province of the highest reason, as it is the basis for the manifestation of consciousness and that which makes any experience possible. What consciousness may be apart from life we do not know. It is, however, quite probable that life and consciousness, so far as we are concerned, are inseparable forms of being. Life everywhere exists in concrete degrees, and qualifies in innumerable forms. So also with consciousness; it appears in the lower forms of life, unfolds into self-consciousness in man, and is already prophetic of higher states and conditions on superior planes of being. It has already been shown in the chapter on matter and force that we do not know the real essence of either. Our knowledge of these is solely concerning relations and manifestations. If in regard to these simpler forms of existing things the essence eludes our knowledge, we cannot expect to grasp it on the topmost round of phenomenal nature. A thorough and comprehensive knowledge of the relations and manifestations of life and consciousness will go very far toward solving the riddle of the Sphynx. This riddle is propounded to every man, if he has intelligence enough to inquire of life its meaning, and of fate his own destiny. It would be entirely beyond the scope of the present work to inquire into the origin of life on this planet. The transmission of life from one organism to another, by which living forms are preserved; the conditions of matter, of force and of structure in which life adheres; and the relations of all these to each other are, however, matters that may be known. The last word of science as to the origin of life is biogenesis. Organisms manifest life; germs develop into organisms; and mature organisms produce germs which again under certain definite conditions develop other organisms, and so complete the cycle of life. This is biogenesis, life created or transmitted from previous life. This is the process now going on, and, so far as we can judge, has been going on from the dawn of creation on this planet. Perhaps no problem has in modern times been more ably discussed and more thoroughly investigated than that of spontaneous generation. This discussion only a few years ago became very animated, and involved many of the ablest minds and the best appliances of the day. In this discussion the endeavor to show that life arises from anything but organisms previously endowed with life failed, and the theory of spontaneous generation was abandoned. Since that time what is called the germ theory has not only become widespread, but it has been introduced into other departments, and now a very large class of diseases are known to originate from and to be transmitted by germs. In another chapter we shall more fully discuss the forms of life, but it may here be stated that in a general sense all germs have an outer physical body, an inner nucleated body, and a still more central germinal area in which life is first manifested, and from which it proceeds outwardly to evolve specific forms or types. Not only does every living organism manifest life and give rise to germs that evolve into organisms, but aside from the manifestation of life by an organism as a whole, and aside from the production of germs, every organism transforms other matter into living matter; and this living matter may be readily distinguished from both the organism and the germ. There are very definite relations between all three. Here, then, are three conditions in which to study the manifestations of life. As the germ may be conceived as containing potentially the organism, or the organism may be conceived to be an expanded germ, we are more directly concerned with living matter and organisms. We may say, in a crude sense, that organisms manifest life and produce germs. They are thus considered merely on the plane of life, above which lie the planes of sensation, feeling, thought, will, imagination and the like. Divested of all these, or rather ignoring all these, what is an organism in relation to the mere quality, life? This reduces the problem to the simplest substance, and the lowest or basic function of life. The simplest substance manifesting life is formless, or structureless living matter. This matter is relatively homogeneous; one part is like every other part, without differentiation. The lowest or initial function of this simple living substance is innate, or spontaneous irritability. This substance so endowed is variously named as biogen, germinal matter, protoplasm, and the like. For our present purpose we shall use the term protoplasm. It is indeed Proteus. It changes continually, responds to the slightest impression, is mobile to the last degree, and is converted into innumerable living forms. The fabled god Proteus, therefore, is its fit representative. This substance, protoplasm, however, is not an organism. It cannot reproduce itself. Neither is it in any sense a germ, though it doubtless constitutes a part of all germs and all organisms. Both germs and organisms have a definite structure and exist as definite forms, while protoplasm is formless. If protoplasm seems to occupy an inferior position, it is, nevertheless, the matrix in which adheres the very life of both germ and organism. Protoplasm is to organism what the ether is to the phenomenal world: namely, the basis of its manifestations, the theater of its display. The manifestation, or functional display of this simple living substance may be summed up in one word, irritability. If this substance so endowed is the basis of the life of the organism, the basic function of the organism is to produce it, and so maintain its own life. This is the process known as nutrition. We are therefore ready to define an organism as a body having such a cellular, or cellulo-vascular structure, that it can take up substances from without, inorganic materials, change their character and convert them into its own structure. The organism thereby nourishes its own structure, and maintains its own life. Nutrition is therefore the basic function of organisms. This is the only definition of an organism that has been found to apply equally to the lowest as to the highest forms of life. An organism defined according to its higher manifestations, as sensation, feeling and the like, would seem to exclude the lower forms of life, though the innate quality of irritability doubtless forms the basis of all higher manifestations. All organisms, whether high or low, must eat and be nourished and reproduce their kind, or become extinct.

It will now be found exceedingly profitable to institute comparisons between living protoplasm and the simplest living organisms. If we institute comparisons between simple living substance and a complex organism like that of man, little resemblance could be traced; the differentiation is too great. There is a group of living structures known as amœbæ. Some of these amœbæ have been described as structureless; there are no visible organs, and apparently little differentiation; placed side by side with a drop of living protoplasm on the slide of a microscope the resemblance is very close indeed, yet are there very marked differences. The amoeba propels itself without organs of locomotion, and swims about in its drop of water like a fish in some land-locked sea. It does not materially change its form except in the act of ingestion of food or reproduction. It literally gets outside of its food, flows around it, encloses it and so assimilates it. In the act of reproduction it becomes quiescent, contracts in the center, divides, and two amœbæ thus result from segmentation of the original structure. The drop of protoplasm, as, for example, the white corpuscle of the blood, has no such independent locomotion, though, as it is impelled onward in the current of the circulation, it appears to creep along the sides of the blood-vessel, and may be seen to pass through its wall. It changes its form continually, elongates to pass into a smaller vessel, and becomes again spherical as it emerges. It throws out prolongations which become blended with adjacent tissues; and finally, as it is seen to pass through the wall of the vessel, it becomes assimilated. One may thus come very near witnessing the very act of nutrition, as we previously witnessed the act of reproduction with the amœbæ.

In dealing only with outlines we must pass by a great deal of interest to the student of biology. The progressive transformation of living substance into tissue, with progressive change of function that accompanies all such change of substance, is called differentiation. Tissue is therefore differentiated protoplasm. All tissues are composed of cells. A cell is a living structure composed of an outer body, an inner nucleated body, and within this a germinal point or area. Nutrition consists, first, in the production of living matter from inorganic, the food; and second, in the transformation of this living matter into tissue. The food is relatively heterogeneous; the protoplasm, relatively homogeneous; and the tissue again heterogeneous.

Bearing in mind now the fact of ceaseless change as pertaining to the very existence of all matter on the visible plane, this change being the necessary result of the persistence of motion, we shall find that change belongs both to what we call dead and living matter. In fact, mobility is greatest in living mater. All stability, therefore, apparent in living forms is unreal. No matter with which we are acquainted is ever permanently endowed with life; for, as we have already seen, mobility and instability, more than any other qualities, distinguish living matter. In regard to organisms like those of man, we cannot say that they are composed of both dead and living matter, but rather of matter that is becoming alive, and of matter that is becoming dead, thus revealing the underlying *potency* of life diffused throughout nature. The body of man, as of other organisms, is the theater of chemical, of vital, and of organic changes. These processes cannot be entirely separated; they interblend, though here and there one or the other may be seen to predominate. All organic processes are therefore chemico-vital, and the body of all living organisms is therefore the seat of continuous correlations of force. If, then, life qualifies in numberless concrete forms, called organisms, it also manifests in varying degrees in living substance. Living substance outwardly, so far as we can observe, is formless, though its internal molecular structure is undoubtedly very complex. The process by which protoplasm is transformed into tissue with concomitant function, and which is called differentiation, is from the very beginning a necrosis. The ascending grade is from non-living matter to protoplasm, or the endowment with life; the descending grade is from protoplasm through the tissue again back to non-living matter. Thus do the molecules and the mass of living matter, like all living forms, run through the cycle of life. The one typifies the other, just as it was shown that an atom typifies a world. The formation of tissue from protoplasm is similar to the formation of a crystal from amorphous mass, namely, a fixation of form through polarization. The older the tissue, the older the organism, the more angular are the outlines; hence the deep lines and sharp angles of age, as compared with the rounded form of youth. The relation of protoplasm to structures like cells, tissues, germs and organisms is thus apparent. It is the living matter out of which they are built, and whose presence, first and last, constitutes their matter of life, but it does not alone constitute the entire conditions of life. It is the basis, not the crown, the subject, not the object. Tissue cells are differentiated protoplasm, and at the center of every living cell is a bit of untransformed protoplasm on which are impressed the germinal force and the typical form of tissue or organism.

In the body of man this living matter is found floating in the blood-vessels and lymphatics, and as constituting the center of tissue cells. In the presence of chloroform, for example, both protoplasm and the amœba lose their mobility and irritability, which are again restored in the presence of oxygen gas.

We have thus witnessed the display of life in the simplest substance and its least complicated form. We have found it herein to consist of complicated matter without fixed form, manifesting great sensitiveness and mobility whereby it readily undergoes transformation, and that it is endowed with irritability which later on develops into sensibility in association with consciousness. We have no evidence of the existence of consciousness outside of a living organism. Aside from the living substance from which organisms are built, we must not lose sight of the fact that the germ that develops into an organism, and has originated from it, is a definite structure. The conditions under which the germ unfolds are the same in kind as those under which the organism itself exists, namely, by out-flowing and in-flowing currents or waves of motion, determining continuously equilibrium or adjustment of external and internal conditions. The very center of this adjustment, the center of the germ, and the central fact in organisms is consciousness. Therefore protoplasm which is endowed with life manifests consciousness, but cannot be said in any sense to originate it. Life and consciousness are associated together like matter and force, and if it be conceived that on the physical plane, in the objective world, consciousness is dependent on life for its manifestation, it may also be conceived that on the spiritual plane, elsewhere considered, life may depend on consciousness for its manifestation. It is not illogical to conceive that while they may be always and everywhere related, they may change places like matter and force in passing from the objective to the subjective plane, from particled to unparticled matter. Life may thus pertain to atomic structure, and consciousness to unparticled matter. The absolute unity of the basis of consciousness in man as related to the senses, and the individual facts of experience strongly support this view. It should be clearly apprehended that neither the fact of life nor the forms of life can ever be rationally explained from the objective side only, and that as a matter of fact the subjective is as real as the objective. The development of man from germ to birth passes through all lower forms. Embryo man is first germ, then mollusk, fish, bird, reptile, mammal, and finally human. So on the other hand, the whole sentiment life of the globe builds upward, climbs continuously toward man, and it is this ideal human type, everywhere prophesied in nature, that is derived from the subjective world, and which overshadows all life. The substance, the fact, the quality of life, therefore, cannot be separated from the organisms that manifest it; and if these are displayed on the objective plane in a material world, it is illogical to deny that they are also displayed on the subjective plane in a spiritual world. One concept is as natural as the other, though the consciousness of man may as yet concern largely the objective. Natural selection may presently give place to divine selection, and man become more fully conscious of the subjective world. Indeed we may thus read the signs of the times.

CHAPTER VI.

By experiment and observation facts have been discovered in regard to that something, be it force or substance, that is called magnetism. The most constant and uniform characteristic of magnetism hitherto discovered is polarity. If we test for magnetism, polarity reveals its presence, and the deflection of the magnetic needle determines also the quality of the magnetism present, according as the positive or negative pole of the needle is attracted or repelled. Polarity, therefore, may be called the sign manual of magnetism. In a simple voltaic battery where magnetism reveals its presence, very definite changes also occur, coincident with the appearance of magnetism. If a piece of zinc and a piece of platinum be immersed in acidulated water and allowed to touch each other, or if they be connected outside by a copper wire, magnetism appears, and the zinc and the water are decomposed; and while the platinum appears to remain unchanged, bubbles of hydrogen gas rise from its surface, showing the decomposition of water there taking place. When a needle or bar of iron is rendered magnetic it perceptibly elongates, and this has been explained as due to the arrangement of the particles of iron or steel, so that their long diameters coincide with that of the bar. In the magnetic bar or needle, the magnetic power appears to be concentrated at the ends. Having determined the presence of magnetism in a needle, the needle becomes a test for the presence of magnetism in another body. If one end of the needle is attracted, the other is repelled. Like poles repel each other, and unlike poles attract. In the center of the needle there is neither attraction nor repulsion, and this center is called the *magnetic equator*. Many theories have been advanced in the effort to determine the nature of magnetism from its phenomena. Among these, Descarte's theory of vortices, in which he embraced magnetic phenomena, and Ampère's idea of minute electrical currents circulating around the atoms of the magnetized body, seem to be included in the latest theories of *dynaspheric* force. Whatever may be the nature of magnetism, we know that it manifests itself to us through matter, and in no other way; and this manifestation consists essentially in the establishment of poles. Magnetism, therefore, as pure force disconnected from matter, is to us unthinkable. Magnetism as the substance lying back of both matter and force, as the potency of each, and the matrix of all things, existing in the bosom of the ether, is not only thinkable but rational.

In this cosmic matrix atoms of matter exist, the intervening spaces bearing a definite relation to the magnetic spaces, and these again bearing a definite relation to the pulsations of the ether. Magnetic ether would therefore constitute the essence of both the matter and force of atoms of all physical substances. From the physical side, magnetic substance would thus constitute both the matter and force of all material existences. Matter and force being regarded as inseparable and indestructible might nevertheless be resolved back into magnetic substance from whence they came. The various special modes of motion designated as heat, light, electricity and the like, so widely manifest in all forms of matter, would thus have a common basis, and the various forms and ratios of motion, and the change in density, relative attraction, and rearrangement in matter would thus find a common denominator in magnetism. The principle of the correlation of force presupposes just this common denominator. The polarity manifest in aggregated atoms of substances like iron or steel, and which can be readily induced and modified, and again removed by artificial means would be explained as definite relations assumed by the atoms of iron or steel toward each other the primal atomic motions being now given a definite form and direction, like waves proceeding in the direction of the long diameter of the mass. The indestructibility of force, and its inseparability from the atoms of matter, presupposes ceaseless motion of the atoms, and therefore the mode of motion can only change so long as either matter of force exists. Neither matter nor force would be destroyed if resolved back into the primal substance, magnetism, though they would cease to be phenomenal, and disappear from the visible world. Polarity implies not only definite conditions and relations of opposite points, like the two ends of a steel bar, but in order to manifest this polarity a center must also be defined, and this definition of a central poise reveals also what has been called diamagnetism, or a subordinate secondary polarity at right angles with the primary. In all living forms the beginning of development is marked by a positing of a life center, and the establishment of definite relations between center and surface. There also result in these cases both the primary and secondary polarizations above referred to, so that in this regard organization is but a higher and more complex form of crystallization, as crystallization is a definite form of polarization.

Now it may reasonably be asked, What induces the definite modes of motion from point to point in matter designated as polarity? We have elsewhere shown that polarization tends always to the fixation of form. In organisms mobility predominates, and polarization is subordinate. As old age advances the condition is reversed; mobility gradually ceases, and the form becomes fixed, and when mobility ceases beyond a certain point life is no longer possible; that is, the waves of motion from center to surface and from surface to center are no longer possible, the center of life ceases, and corporeal death ensues. All living forms no less than all physical existences occur in space and time, in terms of matter, force and motion. This, however, has been shown to be but one side of the cosmic equation, the universal duality. All existences bear a definite relation through the intervening ether to the subjective world, and the phenomenal term of the equation is one member only. We have shown that the pattern after which nature everywhere builds, and the laws which determine her mechanisms, though displayed in matter, are derived from the subjective world. Nature's displays are transcient, phenomenal, but her laws and types are noumenal, not subject to change. This relation of form to substance, of law to process, is a continual striving, a tension, and this is seen in every manifestation of creative energy. On the force-side there is attraction and repulsion; on the matter-side there is the coming forth and the receding back into the unseen world, so that manifestation on the phenomenal plane is synonymous with duality. No matter takes on form, nor changes its form, except through relations established between center and extremities, or center and surface. The cosmic duality is therefore the principle of sex in nature, though it receives that name only in case of organisms. It is the form in which nature builds. Magnetism is everywhere diffused; it manifests its presence as polarity in all creative and constructive processes, and these depend on definite relations of structure, manifested through motion, and as motion proceeds with structure it assumes more and more direct lines or poles. Physical nature solidifies, crystallizes, fossilizes, and holds in its stony grasp the remnants of the life of the globe, in its tendency to fixation of form through polarization. Physical nature is thus the fabled Medusa, turning all living things to stone, and Perseus is still the god of life that triumphs over nature, the winged Hermes with his caduceus and his cap of darkness, invisible for a season yet forever renewing his life.

We have already seen that underlying all processes for

the building up of matter into definite forms there is a marked tendency to polarity. It has furthermore been suggested that this tendency is due to the underlying stratum of magnetism, everywhere diffused, and springing directly from the bosom of the ether. If we regard magnetism as the polarizing tendency, and as everywhere diffused in matter, then polarized atoms would gravitate either toward the positive or the negative pole of the larger mass influencing them. All attractions and repulsions, all affinities and antipathies in nature may thus be explained on the principle of polarity. The terms positive and negative are relative, not absolute. Polarized atoms, or a polarized mass, may easily be conceived as reversing their poles. Hence the term polarization describes only a temporary state in regard to definite relations. A body may be positive to one object and negative to another, for every body is both positive and negative in itself; that is to say, it contains magnetism, and has two poles. Magnetism, *per se,* may be conceived as latent polarity. An isolated atom may be conceived as simply magnetic, but when related to another it may be said to be polarized. Attraction may be conceived as a pulling force exercised in a straight line. The force thus operating between two bodies of any given dimension, large or small, would be a polarization. If an iron bar can be shown to have a positive and a negative end, so must all the atoms of which the bar is composed be conceived as polarized atoms. These atoms associate together, not as positive and negative atoms, but as bipolar atoms, so that the positive pole of one atom is directly related to the negative pole of another. This association of atoms might be likened, in a crude manner, to a row of children facing one way and clasping hands, the right hand of one clasping the left hand of another throughout the series. If now we conceive an atom as globular, and as polarized, this would establish a central axis from opposite points on the surface. If we assume for this same globular atom diamagnetism, the atom will now be four-handed instead of two-handed. In the various tissues of the body we have this principle of polarity abundantly illustrated and abundantly proved. Man as a whole may be called a human magnet, of which the head is the positive pole and the foot the negative. The right and left sides of the body are similarly related, and so with other parts, constituting a complicated series of polarized bodies, mutually dependent and relatively independent, the lesser subordinate to the greater. In the movements of the blood, in the action of the heart, in the contraction of muscles, in short, in all vital processes this principle of polarity is observed. In all chemical changes acids and bases are related to each other and determined by polarity.

"Albumin coagulates at the positive pole where oxygen and a frothy acid liquid are set free; hydrogen appears at the negative pole along with an alkaline liquid."

Nothing has so much to do with life, health, and disease as polarity. Natural polarity of the entire body and of subordinate parts constitutes that harmonious condition called health. A disturbance of this polarity in whole or in part constitutes disease, and is accompanied by distress, resulting finally in disintegration and death. A corpse is a depolarized mass given over to decomposition. Chemism is no longer subservient to vitality and therefore disintegrates and destroys. In atom, molecule, and mass, in ovum, embryo, and organism, this principle of polarity not only obtains, but it also determines the activity, and secures the harmonious relations between parts. Polarity is the universal principle that underlies all attractions, and is the method by which are determined the various organic forms. This principle, as already shown, determines attraction and repulsion, acidity and alkalinity, contraction and relaxation, systole and diastole, the relations between arterial and venous blood upon which the movement of blood depends. In the nervous mechanism this principle is involved in the sensory and motor impulse, and determines the relations of thought to feeling, and of will to desire. Action in any and all of these cases is impossible except as the precursor of reaction, and follows again as a resultant of reaction. Atomic polarity is the epitome of cosmic duality. If now we consider the general appearance of the body as a whole, and contrast its condition and appearance in health with that of one diseased, we shall find that relatively the one condition is positive, the other negative. In health the individual stands erect, the gait is firm and elastic, the eyes are bright, the cheeks flushed, the beat of the heart is firm and steady, and all the internal movements correspond in vigor and vitality. Now reverse all this by shock, disease, or fear: the face is pale, the eyes dull, the head droops, the knees tremble, the gait totters, the heart is unsteady and respiration clogged and feeble. The individual has become altogether negative. The action of all medicines, properly so-called, is upon this same principle; hence the primary and secondary action of drugs, or the action followed by reaction always witnessed where drugs are administered. Polarity is also the basic factor in pathology no less than in physiology and therapeutics. A chill precedes most fevers, local anæmia follows local hyperæmia, restlessness and irritability follow coma; and while normal and moderate action promotes health and perfects development, overaction or abnormal action results in paralysis.

Polarity, moreover, not only determines the relation of the sexes, but determines sex itself. To vivify is to polarize. All our appetites and passions, all experiences in life partake of this dual form. Zest is followed by satiety, enjoyment by indifference, pleasure by pain. One of these conditions presupposes the other; one complements the other. If one has experienced great sorrow he has thereby developed capacity for greater joy, for only so are the lines of experience deepened. Were it not for this principle determining action and reaction, no single experience could ever be repeated, even approximately; a single act would end the drama of life. It is this principle of polarity that secures approximate rest in the midst of unceasing change; and in the presence of unending dissimilarity secures comparative equilibrium. Observation and experience, fact and phenomena reveal this law as everywhere existing and everywhere operating from atom to sun, and from monera to man. It is cosmic and universal. It divides the substance of the whole creation into spirit and matter, the one positive, and the other negative, two poles of one substance. It again divides creative processes into two planes, the subjective, and the objective, and places over against the physical life of the body the spiritual life of the soul. It shows man's nature as equally adhering to the earthly life without and to the heavenly life within. We cannot even conceive of unity without duality, of harmony without melody. The Fatherhood of God involves the Motherhood of Nature—unity in diversity and diversity in unity. *Elohim* is creative duality.

CHAPTER VII.

LIVING FORMS.

The cosmic form in which all things are created and in which all things exist is a universal duality. Both plants and animals reveal this duality as the basis upon which their multiplication and diffusion over the earth depend. Man is created male and female and only as such does he create. The modulus of nature, that is, the pattern and method after which she everywhere builds, is an *ideal man*. Ideal man is man at his best estate, perfected in nature and triumphant in spirit, at peace with himself and in harmony with both God and nature. In ancient writings this archetypal man is called Adam Cadman. Nature everywhere strives after this ideal, and builds after this form. The simplest embodiment of life is prophetic of man. Building everywhere after this pattern, nature reveals the elements of man in process of adjustment and degrees of unfolding. Involution and evolution express the twofold process of the dual law of creation, corresponding to the two planes of existence, the subjective and the objective. Every specific form in nature is itself a duality of matter and force, of body and soul. Every perfect unity is therefore a harmonious duality. Every evolution on the outer plane corresponds to an involution on the inner plane. In every organic living form consciousness is the central fact, toward and from which involution and evolution proceed. The adjustment of these two processes with consciousness constitutes individual experience. The principle of life and the laws of development are the same in all organic forms. Development is, however by concrete degrees and progressively from plane to plane of being. Each higher plane reveals completer form, the elements of which are derived from the lower plane as to function and structure, and from the plane next higher as to type and essence; the former are evolved, the latter involved. Over against the inheritance from below there is always the inspiration from above. Thus is cosmos evolved out of chaos. Thus does spirit brood over matter. Thus are wrought ideal forms out of earthly shapes. There is differentiation from below upward, assimilation from above downward, with consciousness emerging into self-consciousness and finally into divine consciousness in the archetypal man through experience. That which justifies all these conclusions is the law of analogy, proceeding from the facts of experience and observation. Nothing comes by chance; nature builds by law through pure mathematics. Grant for once that nature is at cross-purposes with herself, that for a single moment she forgets her modulus, and creation ceases and confusion reigns. Beyond the plane of animal life the archetype must be a co-worker with the Creator. He is to put away childish things. This is the condition of life on the human-divine plane. On the animal-human plane he is taught by suffering; on the higher plane he suffers that he may teach. Thus man may discern his nature and read his destiny from the experiences of his own soul. He may barter his birthright or claim his inheritance as he wills. Let him cease his inhumanity and his divinity will draw nigh. He can not serve two masters. The weary or the bewildered soul may take refuge in a creed, and rest like a fossil imbedded in a rock, unmindful of the ceaseless generations of life that go throbbing by. The stream never ceases. The sun still shines, and the earth is green, though the fossil senses it not. We may close our eyes to the light and call it darkness, but the great rolling orb of day never ceases to shine. The darkness only is ours, while the sun sheds his light on all. Man, know thyself! for thou art the epitome of all.

> "Flower in the crannied wall,
> I pluck you out of the crannies;
> Hold you here, root and all in my hand,
> Little flower—but if I could understand
> What you are, root and all, and all in all,
> I should know what God, and man is."

The simple matter of life, protoplasm, assumes various forms in morphological processes, thus constituting the animal tissues. There is great similarity in the tissues of all animals; those of the lower animals are coarser than in man, and the organs that these tissues compose are often very rudimentary as compared with the same organs in man, while in some of the lower forms of life the development is finer and more exquisite than in man. Differentiation, as a mere process of complexity, by no means explains the whole of development. It may prove profitable to consider further the process of differentiation in order to determine what it does and what it does not accomplish.

The human embryo in the course of its development passes through the various forms which in lower organisms are relatively fixed types. It is in turn mollusk, fish, reptile, bird, and mammal, before it assumes the distinctly human form. The human therefore includes all lower forms of life. In the definition previously given it may readily be seen that an organism is something more than a body having organs. Indeed, some of the lowest organisms, like the amœba, are entirely destitute of organs, and yet these simple structures perform all the so-called organic functions, namely, those necessary for the maintenance of organic life. They must breathe without lungs, digest without stomachs; circulation is accomplished without heart or blood-vessels, and reproduction without organs of sex. These various functions are performed by the same structure and at the same time.

Respiration consists simply in the exchange of oxygen for carbon dioxide. Digestion consists in the assimilation of food to the likeness of the living structure. Circulation consists in the concentric and eccentric waves to and from the center, and so on. All these functions are performed simultaneously, thus constituting that condition called community of function, namely, one and the same portion of matter engaged at the same time in the performance of many functions, as distinguished from that condition where several organs acting harmoniously perform as many separate functions. Herein may be seen the contrast between community of function and widely differentiated function. Whenever in the development of an organism a portion of the growing structure is set apart for the performance of a separate function, the balance of the structure is thereby relieved from performing that function. Each repetition of the functional act further develops the organ, and further relieves the balance of the structure from the necessity of performing the act as a whole. Exercise of a function develops the organ that performs it at first in a rudimentary manner, till by continued repetition the organ is perfected in structure and function. In the meantime this process of differentiation in regard to any one function induces differentiation in relation to others on account of the twofold process of involution and evolution on which all differentiation and development depend, and on account of the constant tension toward equilibrium. Differentiation begets further differentiation, not only in parts but in the whole. We never find in a healthy individual one organ rudimentary and others well developed. That would constitute an aborted development. The lungs in man, for example, a complicated structure, are not necessarily so on account of the function they have to perform *per se,* but on account of the general complexity of the organism of which they are a part, and in order to maintain the equilibrium of differentiation. The twofold process then, that is, the perfection of the individual organ and function, and relief of the organism as a whole, pushes the development forward; the whole process runs from community of function to specialization of function. A still further principle is involved. As development from lower to higher forms goes on, and as assignment of territory of the growing organism is made to the various organs, till all organic functions are provided for, co-ordinate centers are established to preside over the various functions and the organs that represent them. These centers preserve equilibrium and harmony between the different parts and between the organism and its environment, and are directly related to the unfolding of consciousness through experience. Thus there arises a second group of differentiations, namely, those occurring between the co-ordinating centers and consciousness. The first group pertains to organic functions; the second to sensory-motor and consciousness. The first group is directly involved in the maintenance of individual life. The second group is indirectly so involved, and is directly involved in sensory and intellectual life. The result in the developing structure is that, as the organic functions are provided for, a portion of tissue may be regarded as left over, and not involved in the direct maintenance of the life of the structure. The amount of matter and energy thus accruing represents the cerebral lobes, and the size and development of these determine the plane of life, or degree of development in each individual. These cerebral lobes in the lower animals are the seat and center of consciousness, and they are thus determined by the range of individual experience, differentiation within, and modified environment. Whenever development passes from lower to higher types, culminating on the human plane, the function of co-ordination moves one degree higher. The lower animal is conscious of separate sensations and of individual experiences. The co-ordination of these constitutes self-consciousness. The difference between simple consciousness and self-consciousness is this: in the lower animal, the equilibrium is established between two groups, namely, the organic functions and the sensory-motor functions. In man a third group is added and co-ordinated, namely, the intellectual and reasoning faculties, constituting thus a triad. This last group is rudimentary in animals, and therefore differentiation is below the point where equilibrium can come in. Co-ordination implies equal terms, uniform complexity at all points. Thus consciousness expanded from higher to higher planes at last reaches the plane of self-consciousness. There is the same difference here between plants and animals as between the lower animals and man. Sensation is developed in plants, while consciousness is rudimentary. Sensation and consciousness are developed in the lower animals, while self-consciousness is rudimentary. Sensation, consciousness, and self-consciousness are developed in man while divine-consciousness is still rudimentary. Now this whole process from beginning to end is a differentiation, but, as previously stated, it involves something more than progressive difference of structure and function. It includes the addition of new elements, the assumption of higher offices, the exercise of higher and higher powers. Progression on original lines by no means includes the process or the results. Mere facility gained by repetition, and complexity by differentiation, can never explain that upward pushing of all life toward higher planes of being. Without some other factor differentiation would be as likely to proceed downward as upward.

Simple living substance, protoplasm, is composed of oxygen, hydrogen, carbon, and nitrogen, with sulphur and phosphorus occurring incidentally. The comparatively uniform chemical composition of protoplasm, and the fact that it is continually derived from non-living matter, and the further fact that the matter of life of one organism is convertible into the matter of life of another organism, have led to the conclusion that the life of the earth in all its varied forms is one in kind, though widely differing in degree, and in

range of manifestation. There is a life-tendency, an underlying Potency, diffused throughout all matter, though
the conditions of its manifestations are found only in organisms, and these arise only from germs; these only give rise
to protoplasm, converting it to life from the non-living form.
So far as the mere fact of life is concerned, organisms produce germs and produce protoplasm, and these again give
rise to and maintain organisms. Strictly speaking, the only
really living substance in organisms is the protoplasm, and
while this substance is endowed with life it has no definite
form of its own. It stands thus at the apex of endowment
with life where the ascent from non-living matter ends and
the descent toward dead matter begins. All other matter of
the body is either becoming alive or becoming dead. This
has become alive, and so remains alive till the process of
differentiation begins that converts it into tissue. It is
slowly assimilated, and slowly dies. It differs from the
amœba principally in having no individual life of its own
apart from the organism which produced it. If it already
had form and individuality of its own it could not take on
the form of the various bodily tissues; it would not be Proteus. It is formless, and hence reflects any image, and takes
on any form. We have thus considered the terms and outlined the process of growth and development from the physical side of the equation. These processes are concerned in
the evolution of every living body, but they do not determine the ideal form, or type. This, it is true, is worked out
on the physical plane, but it is involved before it can be
evolved, or rather, evolution and involution proceed coincidently and simultaneously. Over against this whole process
that segregates and differentiates, there is another that ag-
gregates and unifies. The first process concerns the world
of matter and force, and deals with atoms, molecules, and
the like. The second process concerns the world of power
and essential forms, and deals with unparticled substance.
From this subjective world are derived the idea and essen-

tial form, and this is involved, or worked into the growing germ, and the developing individual life. To put the problem in still plainer form and simpler terms, looking at the numberless forms of animal life on the globe as embodiments of the one life in varying degrees of unfolding, we inquire, what is the principle of form and quality, what the idea upon which nature builds, what is she trying to accomplish? We answer, all forms of life below the mammal are fragments of the human; while all mammals are human in a rudimentary form; hence all animal life is either fragmentary or rudimentary human. If now we consider man as the highest on the list of animal existences, and consider the fact that with a relatively uniform physical shape there is observed a very wide range in the degree of development in the human species, and if we also consider the fact that the most highly developed human beings known to us are still imperfect and therefore destined to still higher development, we shall at last arrive at the idea of a far more divinely-human form of life than any now known to us.

There are two general classes of conditions concerned in the growth and development of individual life. These may be designated as conditions of inheritance, and conditions of environment. There is, however, no quality derived by heredity that is definite and lasting. Whether the inherited tendency be good or bad it is a lingering element of a previous personality, and hence a trammel to the individual who in the midst of adverse currents is destined to stem the tide of all such trammels, and adjust his own experiences to his own self-consciousness. In other words, all inherited bias that predetermines individual character belongs to the receding wave flowing backward toward the dawn of consciousness. The whole tendency of individual development is to shake off trammels and stand alone, being thus free to push onward toward the grand ideal. No such *vis a tergo* as inherited bias can account for intellectual strength or spiritual growth. These are due to the *vis a fronte* that leads man upward and onward. They are not and cannot be trammels derived from previous personalities, but are rather broader liberties derived from the universal ideal, and they are apprehended with greater clearness and entered upon with more certainty as the individual experience gains breadth and depth. In other words, the lower forms of life do not contain the ideal perfect form; if they did they would at once and inevitably express it. On the other hand, the unfolding of more perfect forms cannot be imagined as continually approaching an ideal that has already no existence. The ideal is not evolved from below, where it has no existence, but involved from above, where it eternally abides. Hence all heredity, strictly so-called, belongs to the earthly and animal elements, and contains the agencies of its own destruction. All heredity is personal bias. Individuality consists essentially in getting rid of bias, and advancing from the personal toward the universal. If, then, in his advancement toward the ideal form, man must cast off his heredity, so must he also conquer his environment. In no respect does man show in a greater degree his superiority to the animal life below him than in his ability to conquer, change, or ignore the conditions of his environment. Man readily adapts himself to changes of climate, food and occupation that usually destroy animal life and blot out entire species of lower forms. The survival of the fittest is not so much to be regarded as a preservation of the less imperfect, as a leading upward directly toward the more perfect. It makes a great difference which way we face in observing these survivals; whether toward the ideal end, or toward the crude beginning. If in what we call heredity the good only were transmitted, and if in environment larger liberty and broader experience invariably tended toward higher life, then indeed would heredity and environment prove all-sufficient so far as material conditions go. But the evil tendency is inherited as well as the good; vice is as easily transmitted as virtue; and larger opportunity through improved environment often means only greater wickedness. Heredity and environment are thus incidental in the life of man, rather than basic principles necessarily determining his upward progress toward a high ideal. The personal *ego* is determined by bias derived from both heredity and environment. The ideal form of the personal is egotism; its expression is selfishness. The ideal form of the individual is altruism; its expression is charity. The personal is mortal. The individual is eternal. The personal is evolved from below; it recedes and disappears. The individual is involved from above; it advances and endures. The lower self is an evanescent animal, rudimentary, temporal. The higher self is a universal ideal, a perfect individual.

Passing now from the consideration of broad generalizations to more specific applications, we have to deal with the tissue cell, the ovum, seed, or germ, and the colloid. The colloid is the protoplasmic form, relatively homogeneous, structureless, and as we have elsewhere seen, is the matrix out of which all living forms arise. The tissue cell is a more or less perfect type of the original germ; it has, however, no separate life of its own, but is an integral part of a living body. Coming now to the most important of these primary forms, the germ, the vivified *ovum,* we find it passing through the various degrees of sentient life and vital activity. The germ consists of an outer physical body and an inner nucleated body. When vivified, the latent life is converted into the active form. Impregnation is an over-shadowing; a magnetic picture is impressed upon the sensitive proteus, and it begins at once to be involved as the germ evolves on the physical plane. As development goes on, a distinct nucleus appears in the midst of fluidic cell contents, and a cell wall or membrane forms around the whole. The nucleus divides first into two and afterwards into four parts, or nuclei. The form of the first nucleus is that of an oval disc. From the first two of these discs are evolved the organs of animal life, the senso-motor tract, the skin and the like. From the last two are evolved the organs of vegetation or organic life, digestion, reproduction and the like. These discs form in the course of development two leaves, and subsequently four, known as the developing membranes. These membranous layers form at length a tube, or rather a four-layered tube. The tube forms a hood-shaped structure, and again develops discs to run through a somewhat similar process, and finally the developing germ reaches an embryonic form. The whole of the early stage of development before the distinctly embryonic form is reached consists in a multiplication of the essentials of the original nucleus. Each of the several discs, or nuclei, becomes a separate center of development, till at last they all unite under one definite form, the embryonic. The principle of polarity determined the first cleavage of the yelk, and the same principle also determined all subsequent subdivisions, and finally produced the embryonic form with its polar extremities and rudimentary organs. The process thus far is a differentiation, but there is from the first a limiting and form-producing power at work. The endogenous process of cell formation resulting in the mulberry mass is curtailed, otherwise it would go on indefinitely. That which thus limits the evolution in the line of simple differentiation is the involution which meets it at every step. Over against the segregating process above referred to is an aggregating process which hedges it about and keeps it in strict conformity to the species to which the germ belongs. Whence arises this limiting, form-producing tendency? It comes coincident with the evolutionary tendency; both result directly from fertilization; they are the two poles of the life endowment, and both together constitute the quality and the form of life. The original nucleus is the center of the germ. The first two discs are negative to the original nucleus. In turn they become the parents, or are positive to the second two formed. By following the process of further development this fact becomes apparent, as from the first two discs are developed the organs of animal life, the brain, nervous system and the like. These maintain their polar supremacy, and continue as the center from which radiate all future processes of co-ordination, and toward which concentrate all senso-motor impressions. They are the spiritual end of the polarized arc, and finally merge into the cerebral lobes, gravitating toward the positive pole or head of the embryo, while the matter or negative extremity gravitates to the feet. This process is repeated with the whole of the twenty-two discs formed from the first cleavage of the yelk, each group existing in subordinate degree to the primary; and so also with the four tubes till the strictly embryonic form is reached. From this time the development within keeps pace with the growth from without, equilibrium or complete adjustment being the result of coincident evolution of structure and involution of form. The fact of consciousness is coincident with the dawn of individual life, and arises from fertilization which localizes consciousness in the same act that establishes polarity and transmits creative energy to the germ. Impregnation therefore locates a center of life in the germ, and defining the relations of center to surface sets in motion a series of similar acts which finally give rise to the embryo. It is important to note that the initial point in all these complex changes is the nucleus. These changes begin at the center, and are for some time invisible from without. In the case of birds, and in many other forms, as in the case of the development of the chicken from the egg, the process is wholly endogenous, showing that the essential form is impressed on the egg coincident with fertilization. The genesis of cells and the formation of tissue begins, as in the case with the embryo, with the nucleus. This process consists in the cleavage of the yelk or segmentation of the nucleus. This division is symmetrical, dividing the nucleus into two equal parts. These parts are not only of equal size, but of similar contour and of like endowment, as they afterward pass through a similar development. If we say that the molecules constituting the nucleus are held together by attraction, we must now say they are separated by repulsion. But this by no means explains the phenomenon, for such a simple repulsion could be imagined as scattering the molecules in all directions, and this is not what takes place. On the other hand, if we regard the molecules as polarized, and the ovum as having thereby a positive and a negative pole at opposite points on the surface, the act of fertilization fixing a center would convert the waves of motion flowing hitherto from pole to pole into waves flowing from center to surface and from surface to center. As the line of the former polarity would offer greatest resistance to these eccentric and concentric waves, the ovum would become elongated by this resistance, and this is just what happens. We should next have a bipolar mass in place of the former unipolar one. As the hour-glass contraction goes on, the nucleus divides, as does the entire cell, so that when separated each part consists of half the cell and half the nucleus, the latter lying as in the original ovum toward one side. Let it be borne in mind that we are only analyzing the process as it actually occurs, applying the idea of a substratum of magnetism as a tendency to polarization; in other words, we are explaining these processes in terms of polarity. In embryology, where the process of evolution begins as above described, the nucleus divides into two halves; these enlarge, and again each divides as did the original, forming four nuclei; and these four constitute the basis of all future growth. From this point the process changes, and henceforth we have to deal with surfaces, lines, and curves, rather than with spheroids and masses. The living proteus constituting the original nucleus, and divided as above indicated, and upon which were impressed the form and impulse in the fertilizing act, has done its work. New protoplasm is now brought in from surrounding parts; the orbits pass from ellipses to more direct lines; that is, a series of polarities results, subordinate to, but in harmony with one principal polarization of the whole. Neither differentiation nor polarization, however, can account for the embryonic form which at last takes on the human shape, nor is there any factor in evolution that can explain how these arise. We can say in a vague way that the type is transmitted from parent to progeny, and in a general way that it is impressed on the germ in the act of fertilization; but this states only a fact, and in no sense enables us to get one step nearer its comprehension. All the above considerations regarding the germ belong to the evolution of form and structure, but they do not touch the source or origin of that form. These processes of segregation, multiplication, differentiation and polarization are therefore incompetent to explain the origin of form, nor do they contain one element that goes to show how and whence it originates. We must seek the origin of form therefore in some other direction. Bearing in mind what has previously been said of the subjective plane, as that of essential forms, and of the ether as space holding in its broad bosom unparticled substance as well as particled matter, bearing also in mind the fact that all things belong equally to the two planes, the objective and the subjective, we shall now discover where we are to look for the origin of form. It is mirrored on the magneto-etheric basis of the molecular germ, and is progressively involved toward the center, from whence it is evolved toward the surface. It therefore circumscribes and directs the differentiation going on. Fertilization therefore is a double process and includes these various factors, both objective and subjective, and as on the objective plane are found every degree of embodiment and every conceivable shape, so on the subjective plane must exist every conceivable essential form. Co-ordination of the conditions of these at a given point, in an instant of time through laws of rhythm, constitutes the act of fertilization, and therefore determines form.

CHAPTER VIII.

We sometimes hear it stated that magnetism is life. Such a statement, however, is vague and indefinite, and therefore of no practical value. If it be true, as we have endeavored to show, that magnetism subtends all matter, and manifests its presence as the polarizing tendency, seen alike in the formation of crystals and the vital manifestation of organisms, it may then be said to establish the basic conditions on which the bringing forth of living forms depends. Magnetism determines the conditions of duality and lies at the foundation of all living forms. The life principle may be said to pervade all matter, ready to spring forth at any and all points whenever the necessary conditions are established. We have shown this springing forth as proceeding from a germ, and as depending on the process of fertilization. The latent magnetism then begins its work by polarizing the mass. Then differentiation begins by virtue of the ebb and flow established between the subjective and objective planes. The form is involved and the structure evolved, with the germ center of living matter as a *nidus* for these processes. Matter has been shown to manifest life in two conditions, namely, with and without definite form. The first condition is seen in protoplasm, the second in germs and resulting organism, and these two forms have already been shown as inseparable. Germs and organisms therefore involve all known manifestations of life, and while the essence of life still eludes us, the conditions of its manifestations, when accurately defined, are a very great assistance toward the comprehension of all vital problems. The word life conveys no very definite meaning to most persons, as it would seem to convey the idea of an antithesis to death and nothing more. If, however, one digs deep into the conditions and manifestations of the living and the non-living, he will discover that they approach each other by imperceptible degrees, and at last he will find that they are separated by no fast lines, but merge into each other, and that in the larger aspects creation exists as an equation between the non-living and the living, and they continually changing places.

Aside from the cosmic duality represented by the subjective and the objective planes, the manifestation of life occurs on successive planes from lowest to highest forms. From the little zoophyte two planes diverge. Every conceivable form of plant life gives beauty and diversity to the earth on the one hand, and every imaginable animal form gives expression to sentient life on the other. This first separation into planes occurs at the base of each plane, where are seen the simplest manifestations of life. The next plane springs from the apex of the animal series, where, by almost imperceptible degrees, the grosser animal qualities recede and the lowest human attributes begin to appear. All efforts to establish the point of divergence by direct parentage have signally failed, and are still likely to fail, so long as the whole process of the unfolding of living forms is studied from the evolution side only. The solution of this problem awaits the knowledge of the nature and sequel of that which we call death, or of that which occurs on the subjective plane. For this investigation man must bring to bear faculties which as a rule he now possesses only in a rudimentary form. We have thus the plane of plant-life, the plane of animal life in the lower forms, and the plane of human life. While as a whole, and in their larger aspects, these several planes seem wide apart; as already shown, they approach and finally merge the one into the other, not by direct derivation, but by the common diffusion of the life principle and related terms of life substance. In the progressive evolution of structure the lower organisms are prophetic of the higher, while in the specific involution of higher and still higher forms the human inherits from all below. This plane overshadows the lower forms with its own likeness, and is itself prophetic of a diviner form which overshadows it. This principle has previously been pointed out, but it will bear frequent repetition, for if all embodiment of life inevitably tends toward a divine ideal, it is the most important fact within the comprehension of man. The planes of existence to which man is definitely related are thus the following: the physical, the vegetable, the animal, the human, and the divine. Aside from the general relation existing between these planes, individual man derives his body and his powers from these planes by more or less direct inheritance, and manifests characteristics belonging to all of them. He possesses a physical body, has vegetative, or purely organic functions, manifests animal instincts and attributes, shows human qualities, and reveals diviner possibilities. Every human personality is a composite body made up by various degrees of all lower life. He reveals his derivation in the shape of his head, in the contour of his face, in the outlines and pose of his body, and in all his instincts, appetites, passions and feelings. Not only so, but there is in every person a tendency to predominance of derivation, first from one of the above planes, and second a specific animal type is manifested in disposition and facial expression. A careful study of physiognomy will reveal this last-named resemblance. The resemblance of certain human faces to animals is often very marked. It would seem as though all lower planes of life, and every animal, had been precipitated in the vital alembic from which man is created. Herein may be seen the intimate relation that man bears to all surrounding life. Possessing their forms and qualities, he stands as their complete embodiment and representative. The value

and meaning of man's human birthright make him lord over
all life beneath him, while as already pointed out in a previous section, self-consciousness carries the lines of his inheritance to the plane above him, and enables him to reach
forward to a higher than the human plane.   Individuals
might easily be selected representative of types of the physical, the vegetable, the lower animal, and the human plane.
That is to say, in the midst of a mixed inheritance from all
planes, one or another plane would seem to predominate.   It
is also very instructive to study man from this point of view,
as well as from that of animal physiognomy.   There are persons who are mere physical bulks, who merely exist, and
where all other potencies are subsidiary to the mere physical.   There are again others who vegetate, and wherein the
organic functions predominate.   Neither of these types have
any decided moral tone; they are neither good nor bad in
any marked degree.   They have no zest in life beyond its
bare preservation.   They are listless, impotent imbeciles.
There are again personalities in whom the animal predominates.   As types they are above the two already named; they
not only outnumber the former types, but have in all ages
known to history constituted the majority of mankind.   The
principle they have involved is animal egotism.   Self is supreme.   They lack neither zest in life nor moral tone, though
the moral qualities have not a necessary innate coloring.   In
the supremacy of their self-seeking they are rather indifferent than hostile to others.   They have seldom reached the
point when they love evil and create suffering for pure love
of evil.   They perform evil acts for their own imagined
good.   Such but represent the human animalized.   They do
not crowd alone the gutters and dark alleys, and parade in
filth and rags, in ignorance and legal crime, but they are
seen as oft in public marts, in the halls of trade, in the ball-
room and in so-called "polite society."   Whenever and
wherever man lives in his appetites, and is ruled by his passions, wherever he is willing that another should lose in

order that he may gain, at all times and everywhere that egotism triumphs over altruism is man under animal rule and living on the animal plane. The animal in rags takes a purse, steals a chicken, or breaks into a house, and revels in rot and rum, herding with his own degree of the opposite sex. The animal in broadcloth and fine linen steals a railroad, breaks a bank, or steals legally, and rides in his carriage. He sips the choicest wines, and, to indulge his appetites and passions, leads to ruin, desolation, despair, and finally to suicide every unsuspecting girl upon whom he can place his unholy hands. Who dare say that the animal does not predominate in all these? What tiger or hyena destroys like one of these? The more subtle and concealed the form of animalism the more dangerous it is to society. Every human semblance is made to conceal vice and do duty as almoner to crime, and every garb of respectability is used in the masquerade of lust and animal appetite. The criminal in the dock is never half so dangerous to society as the "respectable gentleman" who feeds his lusty soul upon unsuspecting virgins. Whenever really humane men and women will agree to call things by their right names, and when they shall agree to distinguish no longer between the animal in rags and the animal in fashionable dress, then will the animal plane in human affairs begin to be depopulated. If the foregoing reflections shall seem to anyone out of place, let me remind him that there is a strictly physiological basis to every moral principle; that things can be ethically true in human nature and human life only as they are organically true. The organic underlies all human processes, so must the ethical and the moral logically crown our highest deduction. If nature everywhere builds toward higher forms and unfolds toward a diviner ideal, every honest endeavor intelligently put forth to comprehend nature must show a like tendency. It is therefore competent for everyone to inquire to what plane his life is anchored, for he may weigh anchor at will and move to higher levels, but he will have to tear himself away from the siren passions to taste the ambrosia of the immortal islands.

Passing now from the animal plane to the next higher, we come to the human. The human is essentially the humane, and while this plane has its root in the plane of animal life, and derives its substance from a still lower plane, its human characteristics are only revealed as the animal attributes recede. The animal man is a talking animal, while the humane man is a loving, reasoning soul. It is quite evident that human beings may exist on a very low plane, or very near the border that divides the human from the animal, and this even in the midst of a high civilization. It is also evident that from a comparatively high level one may descend to this low plane, and dissipate there the forces that were formerly used on higher planes. To give our subject a still more practical bearing, we may consider the fact that the amount of energy possessed by an individual is as definite as the actual weight of the body at any given time. This energy is derived from the same source as the matter of which the body is composed, namely, the food. A certain amount of this energy is required to maintain the body and keep it in repair. Whenever this reserve energy is being drawn upon there comes the sense of fatigue as a reminder that it should be pushed no further. The entire body more or less participates in all these results. A reasonable amount of exercise, either of local organs or of the entire body, promotes health and development. A change in the mode of exercise, or from one sphere to another, is followed by a sense of rest, as, for example, when walking follows severe mental labor. Habitual exercise of one organ, to the exclusion of general bodily exercise, develops that organ out of all proportion to the rest of the body, and thus in time lays the foundation of disease by permanently destroying the bodily equilibrium. Great muscular development by gymnastic exercise is, therefore, more often an element of weakness than of strength, and may lead to disease rather than to health.

All functional exercise of an organ, whether in moderation or in excess, whether singly or in combination with other organs, exhausts the bodily vitality, and draws on the general fund of life. As a general proposition an organ develops in size and increases in power by exercise, but whenever this development transcends the law of proportion for the individual it becomes an element of weakness, as it mars the efficiency of the whole. Ideal development therefore concerns just proportion in every part, and whether this be ignored through lack of energy, or transcended by overwork in any given direction, the result is practically the same. In the case of an individual capable of lifting five hundred pounds as the limit of his muscular development, this represents the sum of his energy in any other direction, provided he has a healthy and well developed frame. The individual may lift this amount twice, possibly three times, at any given trial, and the next attempt will prove a failure. Now the point we wish to illustrate is this: these five hundred pounds of energy which are available to the individual may be divided between the different planes of the individual's life. They may be used in physical exercise, in sensuous enjoyment, in intellectual work, or in debauchery; or the whole amount of energy may be divided equally or unequally among the different organs of the body. As a matter of fact, this division is just what every person accomplishes, consciously and designedly, or otherwise. We might go further, and show that the amount of energy possessed by any individual in a lifetime is also a definite and predetermined quantity, and that the method of its employment and the quality of work achieved are relatively only under the individual's control. There is a natural order established by nature in the expenditure of energy which leaves it only partially under the control of the individual. First, nature at all times reserves a definite amount for the maintenance of the bodily functions and for natural wear and tear. Second, during early life the continual growth of the body demands both matter and force, and the great activity of children and young people naturally draws heavily on the vital fount. When, however, adult life arrives, caprice or accident often determines the method of the dissipation of energy, if, indeed, there is any method, and so predominance is given to the physical, the animal, or the human attributes, and the entire stock of energy is thus dissipated, day after day and year after year. According to the evident design of nature it is as natural that the intellectual and spiritual faculties should predominate in later life as that the physical and purely sensuous should have the ascendency in youth. There are, however, few natural lives, and hence old age is often deformed, if not also degraded. There is no more valuable thing possessed by any individual than an exalted ideal, toward which he continually aspires, and after which he molds his thoughts and feelings, and forms as best he may his life. If he thus strives to become, rather than to seem, he cannot fail to continually approach nearer and nearer his aim. He will thus find himself above the mere physical, animal, and sensuous planes, and slowly entering on the supra-human. He will not, however, reach this point without a struggle, nor will the real progress that he is conscious of making fill him with conceit or self-righteousness, for if his ideal be high, and his progress toward it real, he will be the rather humiliated than puffed up. The possibilities of further advancement, and the conception of still higher planes of being that open before him, will not dampen his ardor, though they will surely kill his conceit. It is just this conception of the vast possibilities of human life that is needed to kill out *ennui,* and to convert apathy into zest. Life thus becomes worth living for its own sake when its mission becomes plain, and its splendid opportunities are once appreciated. The most direct and certain way of reaching this higher plane is the cultivation of the principle of altruism, both in thought and in life. Narrow indeed is the sweep of vision that is limited to self, and that measures all things by the principle of self-interest, for while the soul is thus self-limited it is impossible for it to conceive of any high ideal or to approach any higher plane of life. The conditions for such advancement lie within, rather than without, and are fortunately made independent of circumstance and condition in life. The opportunity, therefore, is offered to everyone of advancing from height to height of being, and of thus working with nature in the accomplishment of the evident purpose of life.

CHAPTER IX.

In the preceding pages have been considered some of those general principles to which we must continually appeal in any well-directed attempt to understand the nature of man. It is impossible to study man apart from that universal nature in which he is involved and upon which he so continually depends. In common with all nature the body of man is composed of matter and force; therefore an outline of physics seemed necessary in order that all known relations in the physical realm might contribute to an understanding of those more refined conditions that constitute vital manifestations. Certain general principles of biology and morphology have also been introduced for a like purpose, though in neither case has more than a mere outline been attempted, sufficient to show the line of study suggested. The scope of the present work is suggestive, rather than in any sense or in any direction exhaustive. The aim of its author is to suggest better methods in the employment of the large amount of material already on hand, although the methods suggested are by no means new or original, and he is firm in the belief that this change in our methods is all that is required to give more satisfactory results. The object has, however, been rather to unfold than to apply these methods up to the present time. To make a detailed application of the basic principles of the underlying ether, the diffused magnetic substance, and the resulting principle of polarity, would require far more space than this entire work contemplates. Beyond the facts of science and the records of universal experience the logical deductions of analogy alone have aided us. The universality of these principles is at once the plainest and the most valuable deduction possible; for it at once simplifies our subject, amplifies our knowledge, and intensifies our interest. When it has once been discovered that many problems hitherto almost hopelessly obscured, and which have been regarded as impossible of solution, are easy of solution by a different procedure than that generally employed, order springs out of disorder, and discouragement gives place to interest and delight. Assuming only the fact of consciousness, a true knowledge of its relations to the phenomena of life on the one hand, and to the processes of thought and intuition on the other, gives us a working hypothesis where otherwise no solution of the problem of existence would be possible. In the ordinary method employed in such studies it is practically assumed that man is neither more nor less than a highly developed animal, as he is viewed solely from the physico-vital plane. If it be assumed that man has a soul, the burden of proof is shifted to the physical side as though visible forms and physical methods could prove the existence of an invisible entity. In other words, modern science denies a soul to man, and challenges proof of its existence in terms of matter, force and motion apprehensible to the physical senses, forgetting that the physical senses constitute but one side of man's nature as viewed from the center, consciousness. It would be quite as logical, and far more rational, to proceed on the opposite hypothesis, assuming that man has a soul, and requiring physical science to disprove it, particularly as so little real progress has been made in the opposite direction. A better science, however, neither affirms nor denies. Admitting our utter ignorance of the essential nature of anything, it endeavors to apprehend laws and principles, and to discover relations. In the discovery of laws we proceed from the special to the universal, and we thence discover a universe epitomized in a molecule. In order to rightly determine relations things must be put in their proper place, which means that they are to be taken in their natural order, very much as we find them. Classification must follow careful observation; induction and deduction must be complementary, and through all there may be discovered a thread of analogy giving us a clue to the labyrinth. It is a fact in universal experience that the lower nature can never comprehend the higher. The animal in man can never comprehend the divine in man. It is equally a matter of universal experience that the higher can comprehend the lower. When, therefore, from the plane of the animal senses, man looks upward toward the divine, he can aspire; when, however, from the plane of the higher reason and intuition, man views the planes of life below, he may comprehend them if he will. In ordinary life a long experience, extending through many vicissitudes, is requisite in order that we may know a person. In another case the recognition is quick and sure, a glance of the eye, a pressure of the hand, and time and change are as naught. The soul recognizes its kindred by sympathy that is stronger than the ties of blood, and more enduring than time. Here is something that transcends sense-perception; and though it exists among animals, and to some extent among men and women of a low type, its real nature and scope can only be appreciated through the higher nature of man. To call this sympathy is by no means to define it. The most important consideration is that the fact reveals in man a method of direct recognition, or means of knowing beyond the routine of ordinary experience, or of sense-perception, and this direct method of knowing is not confined to the recognition of persons and things, but it extends also to principles and laws, and to abstract truth. It requires in the knower the elements and the experiences which compass the principle or thing to be known, as on the physical plane we find consonant rhythm producing harmony. The recognition of the fact of subjective experience, or of the existence of a subjective plane, is not sufficient. When once it is apprehended that the cosmic duality enters into the life and nature of man, and that man's entire life is an equation of which phenomenal nature constitutes one member only, to which sense-perception is related, the problem of life is placed in the way of solution. Until this principle is clearly discerned the extent and variety of subjective experiences cannot be accurately determined. It makes every difference whether subjective experiences are regarded as incidental, and semi-accidental, or whether they are discovered to be universal, basic, and commensurate with all objective factors in the life of man. Until this principle of equations is discerned it will be useless to discuss the question of priority in the line of cause and effect, as to whether, for example, the soul builds the body, or the body the soul. For with the ordinary procedure from the physical to the metaphysical the whole investigation proceeds from a material basis. The interaction and mutual dependence of soul and body in the orderly process of daily experience is thereby misapprehended, though in general terms it may be admitted. That which in platonic language is termed the descent of the soul into matter has little meaning for the modern scientist, because evolution has set him to regard the processes of life purely as an ascent from lower to higher forms. The idea of an equation is not apprehended wherein evolution is constantly supplemented by involution, and where equilibrium is established as the outgrowth of the cosmic duality.

Enough perhaps has now been said to show the meaning and the application of the methods referred to in our study of man. Man has a twofold nature in common with all created things, under the law of cosmic duality. Man's life, therefore, exists here and now in two worlds, and he is more or less conscious of both. Man is therefore a self-conscious soul, inhabiting a physical and mortal body. What man was heretofore, and what he may be hereafter, concerns us not. What he is now, and what he may here become, are matters of the very first importance, and by no means beyond his plane of knowing. The mechanical structure of the physical body, the substances that enter into the composition of its tissues, and the proportions of these substances in any given case are now quite accurately known. The mechanico-vital functions of the body and its various parts are also known to a considerable extent. Modern biological science has seized every available opportunity and taken advantage of every accident to push its investigations into the hitherto unknown realm of human nature. Not only the ordinary and constantly recurring functions of the human body have been carefully studied, but unusual phenomena occurring under special conditions and in exceptional individuals have been subjected to careful scrutiny. In this way groups of phenomena have been gathered and classified, the existence of which were formerly unknown and unsuspected. If a given phenomenon occurs in a single individual, and but once in a generation, its occurrence is thereby shown to be possible to human nature, and it may occur again, or it may, if desirable, be induced when once its nature and the conditions of its occurrence are understood. It required the light of science and free inquiry to enable us to study such rare occurrences. Certain hysterical and hypnotic epidemics of the middle ages seemed to contemporary physicians altogether miraculous, and were supposed to be due to diabolical possession, which are now readily explained as *hypnotic suggestion*. The startling amount of energy displayed by certain individuals in these epidemics seemed to indicate supernatural power; the poor victims were often delicate women, yet they successfully resisted the force of the strongest men. Making all due allowance for excitement, superstition, and exaggeration, there were beyond all reasonable doubt unusual manifestations and an inexplicable amount of force displayed, and both the nature and the force of these exhibitions were entirely unaccounted for. When, however, we come to understand the real nature of sex, and its relation to what is vaguely termed magnetism, the mystery begins to disappear. In the case of the girl Angelique Cottin, presented to the French Academy by Mons. Arago, the nature and strength of this force was clearly demonstrated. In still more recent times there have doubtless been many similar occurrences, but they have often been so mixed with fraud, and have taken place under such circumstances as to render it exceedingly difficult, if not impossible, to make investigation. When to these considerations is added the fact that the scientific investigator proceeds from a purely materialistic basis, regarding evolution as the one process by which development can occur, it may readily be seen how inadequate are his methods to cope with such phenomena. Scientific conservatism is both necessary and commendable, but scientific nihilism is both unwise and unscientific; it is a misnomer. Until the subjective nature of man is recognized as co-equal and co-extensive with the objective, and until the would-be scientist is ready to discard his prejudices and preconceived notions, and allow facts to tell their own story, he had better leave all such subjects alone; he can but render himself ridiculous, and add nothing to the sum of human knowledge in these directions.

These subjects are referred to at this time because the day of empiricism is well nigh past and the era of real scientific investigation has begun. Even fraud and self-deception have had their day, and the light of a new day has already dawned. At no time since written history began have there accumulated such a wealth of material and such unlimited freedom to investigation. The discoveries of physical science already impinge so closely on the borders of the unseen universe as to reveal glimpses beyond the realm of the ordinary senses. The veil has grown thin, and here and there it has been lifted, separating the external world of effects from the internal world of causes. The power of mind over matter is everywhere being recognized, and the uplifting of the human race to higher planes has already be-

gun. Old riddles are being solved; old traditions are passing away. The nemesis of error and of superstition is the
resurrected genius of truth in the age that is dawning.

The most senseless and terrible of all superstitions is the
manner in which man is in the habit of regarding the beginning and the end of the present life. Life begins often in
a tragedy, and is ushered in by wailing anguish. The chamber of birth is often a chamber of torture, enough to daunt
the stoutest heart, save only the trained physician bent on
his mission of mercy. And yet the tragedy is soon forgotten
amid rejoicings and offerings of flowers. Death is peaceful
and painless, a very foretaste of bliss, as though nature
sought to reward even the weakest and poorest after the
lessons in life which she sets us here to learn. Yet we usher
the soul out of the body with tears and anguish, and drape
in blackness, and mourn where we should rejoice. For this
perversion of the ways of nature we are largely indebted to
the traditions of the dark ages, and to the inherent selfishness derived from the animal plane of egoism. If we could
know all the sorrow and suffering that await the new-born
soul even egotism would fail to make us rejoice in its coming. If we could know the rest and peace of dying even
egotism could not make us mourn. In the new day that is
dawning an infinite pity will possess humanity, and death,
rather than birth, will have garlands of flowers. No wonder
that the little one comes out of its prison-house with a wail
of anguish such as only the agonized mother-heart can understand. How terribly is its little life beset with pains and
dangers, and its early youth with snares and pit-falls! How
many grow weary of the struggle, how many fall by the way!

> "Little lips that never smiled,
>   Little eyes that scarce did see!
> Alas! my little, dear, dead child,
>   Death was thy father and not me;
>   I but embraced thee soon as he."

"O little feet that such long years
Must journey on through hopes and fears,
    Must ache and bleed beneath your load!
I, nearer to the way-side inn,
Where toil shall cease and rest begin,
    Am weary thinking of your load."

If we could know how we trammel these little ones, how we load upon them our sins and infirmities, how we grudge them the poor privilege of being born after we have made birth a necessity; if we could know how we mould their little lives and pre-determine their destiny, we would at least stop and take counsel with ourselves. But a new generation of mothers is coming to the world and the children will be redeemed through them. In the new day that is dawning there will be no little waifs born to disbelief, to rebellion, and to crime; no shrinking, terrified little ones, never sure of a welcome from the cradle to the grave, hungering for love, yet shrinking from it as though every fiber of their lonely lives was steeped in distrust and self-abnegation! What but infinite pity can understand the sorrows of childhood! What but infinite love can reassure these unwelcome children! Physiologists talk learnedly about temperaments, constitutions, and pre-dispositions to disease; and sociologists talk about pre-disposition to crime; and philanthropists, of reform. Education can never correct the defects of birth, nor can restraint or punishment prevent crime, nor reform the criminal. Pre-natal conditions have forestalled all these and given to many lives a bias that nothing can change, a perversity that nothing can materially alter. When once this fact is realized, and when it is also realized how all these lamentable conditions can be prevented, then will earth's humanity be other than it is now. He who attempts to study the human, and is ignorant of this sad chapter in the history of human nature, or he who imagines that he can ignore it and still arrive at any large truths, will find himself mistaken. An adequate knowledge of man takes into account all his faculties, and all his surroundings, the conditions of birth, of parentage, and of inheritance, as a basis upon which to predicate his nature and destiny. These are the very elements of a study of human nature, and it is because these elements are so largely ignored that such unsatisfactory results are generally obtained. Only a bare outline of these elements and the method of study herein suggested has been attempted, but if these suggestions shall prove incentives to more competent investigators the object of the writer will have been accomplished.

The science of anatomy has mapped out the human body as a whole and has also given very concise details of its various parts, so that a clear and exact description of the human mechanism may be obtained. Thus to comprehend the human body, however, requires several years of very careful study, and to this must be added object-lessons in the way of dissections and demonstrations. It is found that the apparent unity of the physical body is due to the harmonious association of parts, and that this association is on the principle of primordial centers, and subordinate relations of other parts of these, and to the whole. These various parts are again composed of microscopic cells, while the cells originate from the simple living substance, protoplasm, the differentiation of which into specific shapes constitutes the cell. It may thus be seen that the body is a community of vital functions, and that these microscopic centers of life associate under definite conditions to produce exact forms. From this association arise the vitality of the body as a whole, the special functions of the different organs, and the tissues of the entire body. The vitality of the entire body depends on the integrity of the individual cells and their harmonious associations. Disturbance of this integrity and harmony arises from innumerable causes operating from within and from without. The result in any given case cannot be predicted by knowing only the cause of disturbance, for not only is the result different in different cases, but it is seldom the same in any individual at different times. One individual may meet with impunity a condition that in another would destroy life, or which the same individual would at another time be unable to bear. One person dies from lock-jaw caused by a prick of a pin. Another may be mutilated almost beyond recognition and yet recover speedily and suffer no great inconvenience. Every case of injury or of disease becomes, therefore, a problem by itself, more or less governed by general laws, yet in no case to be pre-determined. The vital equation is constantly shifting, and with every change a new problem presents itself. This susceptibility of the organism to disease and death is the exact complement of its adaptability to the conditions of life, to more extended experience, and to wider knowledge. It is the uncertainty of the tenure of life that fills the minds of men with superstitious fear, and places the masses at the mercy of the mountebank. It is a matter of great importance and often of very great difficulty to determine when life is really in jeopardy; and, as this question presents itself as a somewhat different problem in every case, only a judgment cultivated by long study and close observation, and fortified by wide experience, can hope to solve it. Even the most cultivated judgment is often at fault, and caution is its marked characteristic. Lucky hits, and happy accidents, often give to ignorance and conceit the garb of wisdom.

The science of anatomy teaches that the body is made up of organs composed of the living cells already mentioned. It is furthermore discovered that certain of these organs are of a similar kind, and so the tissues are also classified into systems of organs. Hence we have the osseous system comprising all the bones of the body; the circulatory system comprising all the blood-vessels of the body with the central heart; the nervous, the glandular, the muscular, the digestive, the lymphatic systems, and so on. While each of these systems is employed in some special office they have a great deal in common. All the tissues are composed of cells, and every cell typifies the entire organism. The difference in the form of the cells determines the tissue of the various organs.

These various systems are again grouped to form two large classes, the organic and the specific. To the organic belong those organs and functions that maintain the bodily structure. These are digestion, absorption, secretion, respiration, circulation and the like. To the specific belong the motor, the sentient, the intellectual and the like. Each cell, each organ, each system contributes something to the good of the entire structure, and receives in turn something from each and from the whole for the maintenance of its own integrity. Health means a perfect adjustment of all these parts and of all relations according to the laws of equilibrium and harmony. We cannot conceive of a single microscopic cell being out of tune without disturbing thereby the harmony of the whole. There is moreover something more than this harmonious association; there is an inter-penetration. The nerves, the blood-vessels and the lymphatics run everywhere and penetrate all other tissues. Every microscopic cell is a station for export and import, receiving nutrient supplies, giving off effete matters. The blood-vessels are thus the highways of a mighty commerce, and from them is derived the significant expression, "the arteries of trade." There is the incoming tide of food, water and oxygen, to say nothing of the effects of light, heat and magnetism. There is also the receding tide of carbon di-oxide, and worn out material; and so nicely is the balance adjusted that, with the several hundred pounds of materials annually thus taken in and given out, the avoirdupois of the body often remains for years the same. Aside from the tissues proper, the more permanent structures of the body, there is thus a large amount of material constantly *in transitu,* and health demands that there shall be no collision between the incoming tide of nutrient material and the outgoing tide of effete matter. Indeed, the mechanism and relations are so nicely adjusted that the presence and movements of the one facilitate the progress of the other. The body of man is thus like a walled city, with innumerable inhabitants that have discovered perpetual motion, and that never rest and never sleep. This is an old idea, and in mystical writings this city is called Jerusalem, Zion, and its nine avenues are called "the gates of the great city."

If we examine the bony skeleton of man separated from all other portions of the body we get but an inadequate idea of the human form. There are cavities like the cranium, thorax and pelvis, mere excavations, with nothing to indicate their previous contents. There is indeed symmetry in contour and an admirable adaptation of parts. The mechanism of the bones of the hands and feet, and the various joints whereby a great variety of motions may be secured, is wonderful. The spinal column seems inadequate to support the trunk and bear aloft the temple of the soul. Little idea of its great flexibility in life can be derived from the denuded spinal column. The skull, with its smooth contour, its grinning teeth and its eyeless sockets so little resembles the head in life that it ceases to be a wonder that it stands throughout all time as the emblem of death. If the entire bony structure of man were withdrawn from the body only a mere pulp, incapable of motion, would remain; the muscles, useless without fulcrums; the tendons, helpless without pulleys.

If now we undertake to examine the muscular system separated from all other parts, we find that it more nearly conforms to the bodily outlines in life; but the connections are wanting. The support and connecting links furnished by the bones, the stimulus of the nerves, the life-giving currents of the blood are wanting, and the muscles are incapable of the least motion.

Considering next the circulatory system, and imagining it to be withdrawn entire from the body, we find it a complicated system of tubes running to and from the heart. The arteries break up or subdivide into arterioles and capillaries, and these again unite to form the venules and then the veins, and so return to the heart. But that wonderful force-pump, the heart, will not work. It requires the stimulus of the nerves to keep it in motion, hence the stream of life is still. The system of blood-vessels shows the contour of the body, so finely divided are its capillary branches, ramifying through all the tissues, and covering the surface of the body so that not a pin's point can find it wanting. In withdrawing the blood-vessels and their contents we have withdrawn but a fraction of the entire weight of the body, yet none of the changes incident to life can go on.

Turning now to the nervous system, the brain and spinal-cord and their appendages, together with the sympathetic nervous system, we shall find that its withdrawal from the body arrests all rhythmic motion, all co-ordination; sensation, feeling and thought are no longer possible. In contour the nervous mechanism might remind one of the human form, though it would equally resemble an overgrown and distorted spider.

The respiratory mechanism does not seem so extensive nor so complicated as the other systems named, unless we consider it as part of the circulatory apparatus, which indeed it is. Nothing can be more intimate than the relations existing between these two mechanisms and their functions. The blood and the air meet and mingle in the lungs. Here is the great motor of life, mechanical and magnetic. All other functions may be arrested or greatly modified and a measure of life continue, but if the functions of the circulatory and respiratory systems are disturbed life at once begins to wane. In all diseases where the individual is liable to sudden death these two structures and their all-important functions are involved. In all diseases tending directly to death these functions are first to give signs of distress. So long as the action of the heart and respiration are normal life is secure; whenever Death approaches from whatever cause, these show the first signs of his coming.

The glandular system of the human body has very important functions to perform. The office of this system is to separate substances from the blood and allow time and space for both composition and decomposition to occur. The products thus arising by separation are of two general classes, called secretions and excretions, the former of use to the system in carrying on its complicated functions, the latter not only waste and worthless, but positively injurious to the individual as well. In some cases only the form of noxious substances is changed and there results a useful secretion.

Back of all the systems and functions named, yet involving them all, is the nutritive system. This may be regarded as the basic function of all life. Nutrition involves the transformation of other substances into living matter, and the maintenance of the integrity of the tissues of the body. All processes of growth, development, repair and vitality are largely questions of nutrition. If we regard nutrition as the basis of life and the central function to which all others are tributary, and yet upon which all depend for their maintenance and integrity, we shall get an idea of its relation and importance. The more direct factors in nutrition are digestion, absorption, circulation, and the final act of assimilation. Regarding the nutritive process as a whole, the most important consideration regarding it is the fact that through its agency nutritive material is converted into living matter. This process is one of progression, beginning in the digestive tract and completed in the glandular system. The substances so formed, the lymph or chyle corpuscles, are in mere endowment of life superior to any other substances in the body. The nutritive function, therefore, lays the physical foundations of life, replenishing its reservoirs and vitalizing its streams.

Having briefly outlined some of the principal systems and organs of which the complex body of man is composed, let us regard then *in situ,* each in its proper place with due relation to one another. We have not yet discovered the mainspring of life. What makes the wheels go round? If we now observe a living man, what do we see? First, he breathes; the lungs expand and contract, and there is the incoming and outgoing tide of air. The expansion and contraction of the heart is synchronous with the action of the lungs, and the blood starts on its busy round supplying life-giving elements to every part, and removing effete matter to be exposed in the lungs to the transforming power of oxygen. The muscles quiver with expectancy, awaiting the thrill of life at command of the will. Life blooms on the cheek; intelligence beams in the eye; emotion dances like a band of nymphs around the mobile mouth, and the conscious soul of man beams in the human face. What have we here not discernible from our previous outlines of the systems and organs? We have motion, visible, rhythmic motion. The breath typifies and illustrates this motion. The regularity with which we breathe in and breathe out is a to-and-fro motion from surface to center, and from center to surface. Thus is expressed and illustrated man's relation to the world about him. He is a self-conscious center of life, adjusting his relations to his surroundings at every breath, and the process of the incoming food and the outgoing *debris* are upon the same principle. We seldom pause to consider how much motion has to do with both the maintenance and the manifestation of life. If we imagine an individual reclining in an easy posture, how do we know whether he is alive or dead? His face is calm, his eyes wide open. Is he conscious or unconscious, alive or dead? Let us see. We address him, and he makes no response; still he may be playing a part, or he may be in a trance. Notice the eyelids; they move not, not a quiver around the sensitive mouth, no visible sign of life, no outward manifestation. We seek the pulse to see if the blood-wave reaches the wrist. It is not there; we drop the ear to the region over the heart, no sound is heard. We rest the hand over the chest, but can detect no rise or fall. We lift an arm, and on letting it go it falls as a dead weight. The case is now desperate. As a last resort we hold a mirror to the mouth, and its brightness is not dimmed by a faint breath; or we press the blood from the surface veins, and it returns not. Alas, he is dead! Trances have been known so deep as to resemble death, but they are the exception and need not be noted here. We thus see that internal molecular and rhythmic motion, and outward visible motion, are the conditions of life and its manifestation. We have here just the conditions that were shown in a previous section to belong to the external world of phenomena. These same conditions also concern the outward manifestation of consciousness, but do not concern consciousness *per se;* for just the conditions above described have occurred, and the individual has preserved the memory of conscious experience thus occurring under altogether different surroundings and conditions.

We have thus sought the mainspring of life in a complicated mechanism by viewing its larger aspects, and by proceeding from without inward. Let us now study man from his beginning.

The body of man in common with all animals and plants originates in a germ. Previous to fertilization the germ resembles a tissue cell. It has no continuous life of its own apart from the body that produced it. Fertilization or impregnation constitutes it an independent center of life, which, under definite conditions, it can maintain and expand. It begins to unfold or evolve as elsewhere described or outlined. Life it had already as endowed by the maternal life. This pre-existing life comprised exceeding mobility, irritability and sensitiveness. There was doubtless latent consciousness, but now it starts on its upward journey toward self-consciousness. Definite relations are established between center and surface; and these relations accompany it in all its subsequent career. The struggle for existence from germ to adult life of man is a continual adjustment between center and surface—between the individual and his environment. The ideal center becomes self-conscious. If this, however, were all, man would be a living cell, large or small, simple or complex, but no more. We have similar organisms, but they are never endowed with the *human form divine.* A single act of impregnation starts the whole process. From the physical side of the problem nutrition and differentiation comprise it. A center of life derives from these two processes that which enables the plant to compass and continue its cycle and maintain it perennially; but they do not account for the specific form even of plants. Grant that the unfolding of this form is progressive both in individuals and in species; but whence arises the definite type toward which progress is continually made? We have already shown that all lower forms of life may be regarded as fragments of the human, and that the higher mammals are rudimentary human beings. What does the act of impregnation do, aside from establishing an independent center of life? It impresses upon the germ the specific character and limitations of the paternal form. This endowment meets the endowment of personality on the physical side at the very center, and the union of these constitutes the germ of self-consciousness, just as the endowment of life on the vegetative plane creates a germ of consciousness The ideal form is an overshadowing presence progressively involved at every stage of growth as the outer structure is evolved. In the human embryo this is the *Adonai,* the shining one. It is an endowment from the subjective world through the spiritual side of man's nature, and so maintains the duality of human existence, and preserves and progressively perfects the human form.

The germ when vivified begins then to unfold. It at first vegetates; cells multiply as in the simplest plant. Membranous expansions of cells arise; then a mere trace indicates the spinal cord and digestive tract. One little mass indicates the location of the brain, inclosing two little vesicles, the rudimentary eyes. Little currents slightly branching show where by and by the pulses shall beat, ebb and flow, and presently on one of these appears a slight expansion, and in this a gentle quivering motion. The elixir works; the magic of life has begun to show forth; the heart has caught the rhythm of the ether and is

> "Keeping time, time, time,
> In a sort of runic rhyme."

By and by the organs are all formed; the miniature man or woman is complete; the beating of the little heart can be heard through the walls of its dark prison. Then comes the throes of anguish, the agony of motherhood. Miraculous changes are rapidly taking place, in heart, in liver, in bloodvessels; old channels are dried up, and new ones formed. Little doors close forever. There comes a gasp, a sigh, a faint wail. The little cheeks are crimson, the chest rises and falls; the wheels of life go round; the miracle is accomplished; a child is born. There is little intelligence in the eyes that shun the light, yet there may be a deeper intelligence of the world from whence the little one comes. Who knows?

> "Who can tell what a baby thinks?
> Who can follow the gossamer links
> By which the manikin feels its way
> Out from the shore of the great unknown,
> Weeping and wailing and all alone?"

All future growth is but a continuation of processes already begun. No principle can be discovered in the life of man that has not here its root and rise. The dawn of consciousness, the growth of intelligence, the manifestation of life through co-ordinate rhythm establishing that equilibrium we call health, all these have their potency and prophecy in the vivified germ. Millions of times this miracle is repeated, yet millions regard it with indifference. Accident, caprice, or blind lust determines it ten thousand times where love and wise forethought provide for it but once. Nativities are saturated with murder and marked by paternal thoughts that are crimes. Little helpless souls are thus scarred all over, and evil destinies are thus heaped upon them from their very birth. O horrible reproach on the divine office of parentage! And yet we wonder at perversity, at wickedness and at crime, and build almshouses and prisons, asylums for the insane, and homes for the multiplicity of our abominations, and then credit ourselves with Christian charity! Even yet our boasted civilization has not done with these waifs of time, brought here without their consent, denied the royal welcome which is theirs by divine right. Unwelcome, perverse, bearing the sins of matured wickedness in their frail bodies, hedged about, handicapped by the very Medusa's helmet, terrified, bewildered, it would seem that the measure of our iniquity were full and their damnation complete. But no, we summon the sacred name and garb of religion and follow them into the unseen and unknown. Having perfected the tragedy called life, we crown peaceful, silent, beneficent death with fear and despair! If you deny this portraiture, my brother, my sister, tell us whence this surging mass that fill our prisons and insane asylums? Whence the larger mass that scout the very name of religion, that clamor for work, for bread? Whence come the mobs, the anarchists, the murderers, the suicides? Count these millions in our boasted civilization, and call it Christian if you can. There is but one single cause for all this misery of human life, and it can be spoken in one word, *egotism*. It arises from ingrained selfishness, derived from the animal in man, forgetting all good for the sake of self. Selfish passion, a moment's pleasure and an age of pain, selfish greed, the survival of the fittest, what are these but the *shibboleth* of the devil, the slogan of the infernal regions? It is not a hell *for* man, but a hell *in* man, created *by* man. "Human beings are not fit to be parents till they are *morally of age,* and as being is before knowing and doing, I affirm that education can never repair the defects of birth."* It has been elsewhere shown that all inherited bias pertains to the temporary personality of man, and that the self-conscious individuality has to get rid of the evil heritage, and confirm and co-ordinate the virtuous heritage by use in order to make it his own. There is no subject that lies so near the cause of all human ills, and that is so potent a factor in the regeneration of the human race as the conditions of parentage and the influence of so-called heredity, or natal and ante-natal conditions. Whenever as much care and forethought are bestowed on the begetting of children as upon the breeding of horses and cattle, a new order of humanity will appear on the earth. If the reader is disposed to ridicule such plain speaking, let him first ask himself whether these considerations are not true. Having satisfied himself on this point, as a mere matter of intelligence, he may ridicule or approve as seemeth to him best.

Having briefly outlined the process by which the fertilized germ develops into a child, by evolution of the bodily structure and involution of the human form, and having arrived at the basis of all subsequent function, all human qualities which exist potentially in the child, we shall find that the conditions of further unfolding are the same in kind as in the embryo, though differing in form and conditions. From germ to birth the process is continuous, though it seems to be marked by distinct stages. Between these various stages there are, however, no abrupt transitions. Each preceding stage leads up by imperceptible degrees to the one that follows. Take, for example, the nutritive changes. First we have the merely vegetative form of cell multiplication and cell nutrition. As the embryonic

*James Pierpont Greaves.

life advances this form of nutrition is replaced by what is known as tuft nutrition. This again gives place to placental nutrition, and this again to lactation after the birth of the child. These various changes or stages of nutrition relate to the method and mechanism by which the nutritive material is elaborated or raised from non-living to living matter. In plain terms the only question is: Where does the germ, the embryo, the fœtus and the child get its food? In all these cases the answer is: from the maternal body. The process called weaning is the most abrupt and radical of all these nutritive changes. Henceforth the child manufactures its own matter-of-life, raises so-called dead matter to the form called living-biogen. The process by which this living matter is differentiated into tissues and organs is from first to last the same. The process by which a tissue, an organ or an entire organism is built, is the same process by which when built these all continue to act. In other words, the basic principle behind all function is the principle which determines growth and development of structure. The function builds the organ; the organ exercises the function; the principle of sound builds the ear; the principle of light builds the eye; the principle upon which thought proceeds builds the brain, and so on, else organ and function would not be so definitely related. The act of impregnation sets in motion the wheels of life. Evolution of the physical structure begins. Mobility and irritability of the living matter at the center of the germ, the nucleolus, or germinal spot, are progressively unfolded and differentiated, evolved from center to surface. These outgoing waves and impulses are met and limited by ingoing waves that determine the form, limit and direct the unfolding of the germ. Between these two groups of impulses there is continual adjustment, equilibrium. Previous to impregnation the germ is a simple cell, detached it is true from the maternal body, conditioned so that it can take on an individual existence of its own; yet without the fertilizing process it speedily dies. The genesis of individual life on the physical side is coincident with the endowment of specific form on the spiritual side. There hence arises a tension between these processes, and at the center, where both unite, there is a poise. Irritability of living matter reaches the sensibility of a growing organism, thence proceeds consciousness in the advanced fœtus, and finally self-consciousness dawns in the child. At birth the organs are all formed. The child is a man or a woman in miniature. The process continues; by the same process of differentiation and evolution on the one side, and of progressive involution on the other, the child expands toward maturity. The most important factor herein disclosed is consciousness. Potentially it is transmitted like the quality of life itself to the germ. We may say *senso-genesis* and *conscio-genesis,* as well as *bio-genesis.* Self-consciousness, however, is a condition that transcends and co-ordinates all lower forms. It is a strictly human attribute. It is the result of man's larger and more complete relations to nature on a superior plane. Man reaches this plane only by passing through and beyond all lower planes. As already pointed out, all lower forms of life, in form and quality, are fragmentarily human. The higher mammals are rudimentarily human. Man only embodies them all. Every human being passes through these forms in his embryonic and fœtal journey toward self-consciousness, so that the principle is true in humanity at large and in every individual case. It was previously stated that all knowledge is derived through experience. Herein may be seen man's journey of experience, his kinship with all lower nature. His experience on the human plane is the *concensus* of the experience of all lower forms of life, not theoretically, but actually. The self-consciousness of man is therefore the combined experience of the whole world of plants and animals. One might say in all truth and soberness: "Only a few years ago I was vegetating; a little later I was a mollusk; then a fish swimming in a soul-locked sea; and a little later I was a reptile, a bird, a mammal, and now a man." Memory only is wanting. He has forgotten these experiences just as he has ten thousand others since he was born. Every physiologist will say that this is true; that so far as conditions and relations are known these are the physiological facts. But a still further and far more important inference remains to be drawn. If self-consciousness in man implies a concensus of all lower forms of experience, is there not a still higher human plane? Is there not a state in which man rises to a higher plane, where the individual through sympathy and love may become the concensus of humanity, and so reach divine consciousness, an all-consoling sympathy, an all-embracing love? In this state may we not remember those who are bound as though bound with them, mourning with those who mourn, rejoicing with those that rejoice, the animal egotism giving place to the divine altruism? This is the true meaning of *Christos.* What we call the human is an intermediate stage between the animal and the divine. The body of man then is a human form in which to unfold divine attributes—a wayside inn in the upward journey of the soul. We may study man to some purpose if we will, and learn the meaning of life and the destiny of the soul. To do this we must honor every truth by use, and learn here as elsewhere by experience. Blind superstition and ignorant credulity have had their day, so has materialistic science. A diviner science awaits him who places truth above all things, for all truth is given by inspiration, and all truth is divine. The true, the good, and God are *one.* Man learns these as he learns to know pain and pleasure, by experience.

The human body does not necessarily imply human qualities. In a certain sense man is only a higher animal. We may degrade every human attribute to the very lowest animal plane. Destruction, rapacity and cruelty, coupled with the human consciousness and intelligence, are in no sense human. The essentially human is the humane; and in this regard many of the lower animals in affection and faithfulness, even in the face of abuse and cruelty, might cause many a man to blush for his inhumanity. The most fitting associates for many persons would be the tiger, the hyena or the snake. This is neither more nor less than the development of the animal ego, and the more common forms of lust and greed may be a little less animal, but scarcely more humane. Selfishness is the root of all these, and this is essentially brutal and not human. We have seen that polarization implies a tension between two points, ideally a straight line having two extremities and a wave of motion between these. Aside from matter, force and motion, we have the idea of form, and this again includes molecular motion and differentiation. All these are concomitants of polarity. A magnetic needle is a piece of steel rhythmically adjusted to the polar magnetic wave, and mechanically free to maintain this relation in the face of all oscillations. Its horizontal position presents the line of least attraction to the terrestrial magnetism. The human body is composed of an innumerable number of polarized cells. The grouping of these cells is according to the principle of polarity. The body of man as a whole is magnetic, and consists of a series of magnets, the poles of which are systematically yet subordinately arranged. The magnetic centers of the body are many, and the supremacy of any given center may be fixed or temporary. It may be the cerebral center that governs at one time, the sexual center at another, the gustatory at another, and so on. There are also centers of vitality proper, as the heart and lungs connected with the medulla. The cerebellum is a co-ordinating center of muscular motion. The solar plexus and spleen are related together as the true magnetic center, while the cerebrum is a co-ordinating center of centers. The relation of the human body to the earth is entirely different when it is prone and when it is erect. In the one case the correlative earth's magnetism is related to the diamagnetism of man; in the other, to magnetism proper. In the prone position we may be said to absorb magnetism;

in the upright position we dissipate it. In Von Reichenbach's experiments a stream of light was seen to issue from the eyes, from the hands and feet, from the genital and gastric regions. In some cases this magnetic light has been seen to stream from the back of the head and fill the room. Of the normal body as a whole the head is positive and the feet negative; the right hand is positive, the left negative, and so on. The arterial blood is positive and the venous negative, and the heart is an electro-motor by virtue of the presence and tidal waves of red and blue blood. The contraction and relaxation of muscle becomes possible through the circulation by which the muscular tension is renewed. Every muscle is to some extent a storage-battery. These points might be multiplied almost without end. Our object is only to demonstrate the existence of the principle of polarity and to illustrate its mode of action.

Terrestrial magnetism separates the androgynous shoot in the germinating seed, and sends the male element deep into the bowels of the earth, and the female element up into the air with its potency of leaf and flower and its prophecy of fruit and seed. The tree is thus anchored to the earth, and its polarity is thus fixed. Quadrupeds and all other lower animals maintain a comparatively uniform magnetic relation to the earth and their surroundings. Man alone is an upright animal, a center of life, and a law unto himself commensurate with knowledge. Man's relation to surrounding nature is thus positive in a far higher degree than that of any other animal. He commands the forces of nature, adjusts himself to her varying moods, and thus conquers through obedience to her laws. Nature steadfastly refuses to be subordinated in any other way. In a certain large sense man is therefore positive in his relations to nature, and the degree in which he is able to maintain this relation is, as already stated, in direct proportion to his knowledge and obedience to law. The degree of this positive relation of man to nature determines temperament, health, vigor and his relation to his fellow-men. It is moreover the foundation of sex and the relation of the sexes to each other. The positive man triumphs over the negative, who is the weaker element. Motive gives color to the result of this domination, but does not determine the fact. As a rule man is positive and woman negative as related to each other, though notable exceptions can be found. This is the normal relation, and they may be equal in power notwithstanding this relation, for woman naturally triumphs through the affectional nature, and man through the intellectual. The higher the individual in the scale of being, the more these two natures are united in him or in her. The very variableness of these conditions and relations enables man to adjust himself to his surroundings and to triumph over all lower forms of life. To illustrate man's positive relations to nature, let us imagine a well-born, well-developed individual in health. Health blooms in the cheeks, intelligence in his eyes; reason sits enthroned on his brow; strength and elasticity are in his step, and courage and cheerfulness are in his voice. He is born to command, to triumph, to endure. Imagine now that he is suddenly alarmed, terrified. His cheeks grow pale; his eyes, dull and staring, his hair stands endwise; a chill creeps over his flesh, his knees tremble, his voice falters or fails; his heart flutters, and his breath comes with a gasp or a shriek. A mere mental emotion has instantly conquered more swift and sure than Delilah. Samson is shorn of his strength. The man has suddenly reversed his whole relation to external nature. This negative condition is produced in part or in whole, in greater or less degree, by a great variety of causes. It is more or less approximated by the scenes and influences of night that succeeds the day, and by the innumerable predisposing causes of disease—all excesses, all forms of dissipation, and all previous disease. Therefore, fear or any other cause that produces this negative condition invites disease. Anything that disturbs the equilibrium and harmony of the body as a whole, or in part, begets disease and tends toward dissolution. Not only habits of body, but habits of thought may thus be classed as conservative or destructive. The habitual indulgence of envy, hatred, avarice or lust, tends to the promotion of bodily disease; while pure and noble thoughts, and the exercise of love and kindness, promote life and health and insure happiness, even in a strictly physiological sense.

Through the great dual law of action and reaction man is enabled to regain his lost equilibrium, though frequent repetition of disturbing influences weakens resistance and tends to the fixation of the evil habit. As shown under the law of differentiation, the complexity of any organ in man is not a necessity *per se,* so far as the special function is concerned; but is rendered necessary by the complexity of the organism of which it is a part, on the principle of equilibrium and general harmony of the whole individual. These relations of parts to the whole, and of the whole organism to its environment, whereby equilibrium is secured and harmony maintained through primordial and subordinate centers, are bound to one another by definite ratios. The principle is the same as that which underlies the whole science of music. Indeed every principle in nature is epitomized in man, according to the plane of his ascent and development. There is in nature a unit of space, a unit of time, a unit of matter, of force and of motion; and there is a common multiple of all these which justly contains them all. How else could harmony result anywhere, and nature unfold on a uniform plan? This common multiple exists in man as the keynote of his life, determining the pitch and quality, the major or the minor character of his being. This principle may be most readily illustrated by the functions of the lungs and heart, and their relations to each other and to the rest of the organism. Both these functions vary in different individuals. The beating of the heart is modified by many causes, as is also the respiration; but in general terms the respiration is to the heart's action as one to four. In modern life there will generally be found a fraction in favor of the heart, but this is due to the immense strain that is put upon that organ by nervous excitement and unnatural modes of life. In these two organs with their complicated functions may be centered many of the essentials of life. These functions determine the rhythm, the pitch and the quality of the physical life of man. These processes, respiration and circulation, if rightly interpreted, may furnish a coefficient of the individual life. They are the mathematical basis, and may lead to the metaphysical basis, just as we find *biogen* the physical basis, giving rise to form by differentiation. In health we inhale and exhale with perfect regularity. This simple process illustrates the whole mechanism of man as a complex being. If we could witness the process that occurs in the pulmonary capillaries we should see a pulsating mass composed of tubes, enlarging and contracting rhythmically, and at the climax of expansion instantly changing color from a dull leaden blue to a living—nay, luminous crimson, as though the bellows were regularly applied to the smoldering embers of life. Sleeping or waking this process goes on, from the first faint gasp of the new-born child to the last breath of the centogenarian. The elements or equivalents of force which maintain this wonderful process are derived directly from the great solar plexus, while the rhythmic power, co-ordinating these activities with all other functions of the body, is derived from the brain and spinal cord through the pneumo-gastric and cerebro-spinal centers. Through these last named structures the chemism of the body is subordinated to its vitality; and with the control of the sweat-glands and general excretory outlets, and the epithelial tissues aided by the thermic nerves, the temperature is maintained with most remarkable uniformity. This process that we have imagined as witnessed in the lungs is continued to the remotest elements of the body. If we could witness the display of the body's finer forces we should see it expand and contract at every breath, and rhythmically brighten, as if a human glow-worm. We know as a matter of fact that the magnetic power of the body is largely and immediately increased by slow, deep inspirations, and that this accumulative power can thus be thrown from the hands upon a sensitive person in sensible quantities producing marked effects.

This to-and-fro respiratory motion may be taken as representative of the entire bodily functions. Large quantities of food and drink are taken in and an equivalent given off continually, so that the physical as well as the physiological and psychical equilibrium is maintained. Here then is the operation of a twofold law, attraction and repulsion, inspiration and expiration, oxidation and de-oxidation, expansion and contraction, diastole and systole, sensation and motion—all these operations illustrating the law that lies at the very foundation of the manifestation of life. This is the principle of universal duality. Its operation is like the swinging of a pendulum; just so far as the oscillation proceeds in one direction, just so far must it go in the opposite direction, and with equal force and velocity, else all the wheels of life run down and time for man ceases. This principle of duality lies at the foundation of every function of man, is the basis of all pathology, and in every case determines drug action. There is always action and reaction, and these are ideally but not mechanically equal. It is because they are unequal, in fact, that man sickens and dies before his time. To secure this exact equality is the secret of perpetual youth. Every vital problem, therefore, in health or in disease, presents itself as an equation to be solved. The somnolence produced by opium is succeeded by insomnia; stimulation is followed by depression; excitement is followed by lassitude. The manifestation of these effects may sometimes seem unequal. Sometimes the reaction may seem out of all proportion to the primary action. This is because in one case the effect is precipitated on a single organ or a single group, and in the other case it is diffused over wider areas. It is as though one member of the equation were a unit and the other member a series of fractions reducible to the same unit. Another apparent exception is seen in youth and old age. The recuperative power in the one case and the waning vitality in the other do not annul the equation, but merely alter the form of its members and modify the true method of solution, the principle is the same. In youth there is a reserve of physical power, the vital reservoir is full. In the decline of life the physical forces fail but the higher powers ripen. The planes of life are naturally reversed in youth and age, not only as regards the physical and rational faculties, but this reversal involves the sensuous and spiritual powers as well. The poet Heine has beautifully expressed this change:

> "Warm summer dwells upon thy cheek
>   And in thy laughing eyes;
> While in thy little heart, fair child,
>   Cold, frosty winter lies.
>
> But these I think as time rolls on
>   Will play a different part;
> Then winter on thy cheek shall be,
>   And summer in thy heart."

Let us now briefly examine some of the functions of the body. These are divided into two general groups. In the first category are placed those that are directly concerned in the maintenance of the bodily structure; such as digestion, absorption, secretion, circulation, respiration and reproduction. These are called organic functions. In the other category are placed all other functions, and these, while indirectly concerned in the maintenance of the bodily life, are concerned with higher and more special offices. To these belong sensation, muscular motion, thought, and all the higher mental operations, and more especially the coordinating function of the nerve centers. These last named secure the equilibrium and harmony of the whole organism through an equable distribution of energy, both as regards dissipation and the conservation of force.

All function implies motion, and this motion may be visible, bodily motion, or internal, perceptible motion, like that of the heart and pulse-wave; or again, it may consist of imperceptible molecular motion, like that present in processes of digestion, oxidation, nutrition and the like.

The manifestation of life and the exercise of function alike depend on motion, and are equally phenomenal. Let us suppose that we have under observation an individual in health, and in a passive condition; that is, with all the organs quiescent; the bodily temperature is normal, the breathing quiet and regular, the heart's action rhythmical, and the circulation equable. Now let us introduce food into this individual's stomach; this will be the signal for very marked changes to occur. The color of the stomach changes from a pale pinkish hue to a crimson; it becomes thickened and roughened. If a delicate thermometer were now applied to the coat of the stomach there would be found a perceptible rise in temperature. If the gastric blood-vessels are examined they will be found engorged, and the general circulation and the heart's action will be found to be accelerated. By this time there is a flow from the mouths of the gastric follicles of gastric juice. This is incorporated with the food, and digestion has begun. The signal for all these changes is the mere presence of food in the stomach. The presence of an indigestible substance, or the irritating of the stomach with a stick, would produce similar results. There is a change in color, change in the thickness of the coat of the stomach, increase of blood, increased chemical action, and hence increased temperature. During this process there is a withdrawal both of blood and of energy from the entire organism to be focused on the stomach, which is now the center of activity. Digestion in the stomach being completed, the stomach is emptied of its contents and resumes its normal quiescent condition, while the center of activity passes down, accompanying the food along the digestive tract, till the resultants of digestion enter the blood. If this activity of the stomach is unduly prolonged, if too much food or indigestible food be taken, every degree that the stomach is rendered active beyond the normal point, as to time or quantity of activity, constitutes functional disease, the difference between normal and abnormal activity being solely one of degree. In the one case the action is called physiological; in the other, unphysiological. Herein are seen both the conditions and phenomena of all physiological activity, no matter what tissues or organs are involved. Even the function of the brain and the process of thought are no exception. Functional activity implies an increase of blood to the part acting, therefore increased size and increased color; increased activity, therefore more rapid oxidation, chemism, and this increased activity is followed by lassitude or a measure of exhaustion calling for rest. Likewise in all cases normal activity is physiological, abnormal activity is unphysiological, constituting functional disorder, which, when oft repeated or long continued, extends to permanent derangement of structure. Functional activity merges in functional disorder, and this into chronic disturbance of function and finally into organic disease. Again, in the functional changes observed in the stomach we have all the symptoms of inflammation here as elsewhere, function falls short of inflammation only in degree. In either case the tendency is for the phenomena to subside and for the equilibrium to be restored. Whenever the restorative process is unduly prolonged and unusually difficult, and the recuperative energy of the organism begins to fail, the result is fever. The entire organism thus participates in the disturbance. The primary conditions are now manifest on a larger scale. Inflammation and fever indicate disturbance, but they in no sense constitute disease, but rather should be regarded as local and general efforts to get rid of disease. An organism that is incapable of inflammation and fever is incapable of maintaining its own integrity. Such an organism is not long capable of life. Without inflammation no wound unites. The point of perfect health is indicated when the local inflammation is exactly sufficient to unite the wound and no more. In such cases the repair seems almost miraculous. Perfect health is however somewhat rare. In such cases, where there is general disturbance and fever, from whatsoever cause, immediately preceding the rise in temperature there is an interval of general depression, and in very many cases a chill. The fever is a reaction from this depressed condition, and depression again follows the fever in its subsidence. The oscillations become less marked till equilibrium is restored. These oscillations of depression and elevation, of chill and fever, are characteristic of all acute inflammations and of all fevers, though they are sometimes so slight as to elude observation depending in such cases on a large degree of vitality. The measure and degree of danger in all subsequent conditions is thus often indicated by the severity of the chill, though here again, if the oscillations be extreme and the vitality be great, the disturbance all the sooner subsides. It may thus be seen that every case of disturbed function or disease is complete in itself, and to be judged and measured by itself, though occurring under the form of the general vital equation, the duality of nature.

Medical writers have found great difficulty in defining fever just in proportion as their theories have allowed them to forget the conditions and manifestation of all functional activity. Inasmuch as both functional activity and pathological disturbance or inflammation produce local exhaustion requiring rest, removal of disintegrated matter and repair by nutrition; so is the chill that precedes fever an approximate death of the whole bodily structure, and the elevated temperature that follows is due to the more rapid oxidation requisite to remove effete matter, and the loss of strength and flesh so manifest in long-continued fevers is thus explained. Sometimes the slowly waning tide of life is a long time in reaching the point where fever begins, but the principle is the same. Causes and conditions vary, and hence the results vary in intensity and in time, but the law is always the same. Action followed by reaction, reaction followed again by action, till equilibrium is restored, or till death results. Differences in age, in sex, in temperament, in natural vitality, in inherited or acquired pre-disposition, differences in climate, in occupation, in modes of thought, in aims of life, and, even more than all these, differences in the intensity of the *will to live* go far toward determining results, not only in life, but in all disturbances of function or vitality of tissues. Without a knowledge of these facts no adequate conception of the nature of man is possible. Even a knowledge of the essential nature of the soul, such as no one in modern life possesses, would still be deficient if lacking a knowledge of the conditions under which the soul lives and acts in the human body, and in relation to its present environment in a world of phenomena.

The law of action may readily be determined; the conditions and results of action are to be determined in each individual case, and in every moment of time. These results of varied experience are precipitated in consciousness as in an alembic; the original details of experience may be blotted out forever. None know, and none need care so long as we have still their full equivalent.

CHAPTER X.

In a previous section reference was made to the principles of differentiation and the community of function in the evolution of organisms and of species. Through the operation of these principles it was shown how reserved areas arise that are not directly involved in organic functions, and that these areas constitute co-ordinating centers preserving the harmony of the lower structures and functions, and destined to still higher offices in the special economy of man. It was further pointed out that the complexity of an organ and its functions is not a direct necessity of the function to be performed *per se,* but that such complexity is rendered necessary by the general complexity of the entire organism of which it forms a part. Only thus could equilibrium be established and harmony result. This complexity, in whole and in part, is evolved progressively from simple forms in which the given function was still performed. Indeed the function must have existed potentially in the vivified germ prior to all organs proper.

Under the head of Physical Synthesis, Herbert Spencer has shown very clearly the process by which nervous tissue may arise by the successive passage of waves of motion through a mass of colloids. These waves pursue a definite direction following the line of least resistance. Each successive wave of motion meets with less and less resistance, and hence a larger amount of energy is continually transmitted through the line of colloids. The polarized colloids are thus progressively wheeled into line of polar arrangement. A considerable amount of energy is thus used in bringing this about; but this amount is constantly becoming less and less as the amount of energy transmitted becomes greater, till at last a line of colloids is arranged in polar agreement; resistance has ceased and the highest transmission of power is attained. If we conceive that polarity arises coincident with the development of tissue, and not after cells are formed, we shall realize that which undoubtedly occurs as above illustrated. This principle of polar arrangement not only obtains in the development of the nerve fibers, in the building up of nerve tissue, but in all subsequent transmission of the nerve impulse after birth, whereby we gain facility in muscular manipulation and are enabled to cultivate the senses; the process may be seen to be the same. Repeated transmission overcomes resistance and increases the accumulative result. Hence the process by which tissue is formed and by which function originates is that also by which it is afterward perfected and exercised. The function *per se* builds the tissue and the organ; the organ so built exercises the function. Living matter involves the peculiar function; the function so involved evolves the tissue and the organ. The principle under consideration may be called the physical basis of education.

The basic function of simple living matter is irritability. Living matter responds to an irritant and reacts upon all received impressions. It is sensitive in the same sense but in infinitely larger degree than the photographer's plate. Proteus quivers with life and mirrors all impressions. Organization fixes these impressions. Sensibility passes beyond mere sensitiveness by the addition of consciousness. Consciousness implies a center of life; the universal with the added element of consciousness becomes individual. Simple living matter is an element of an organism, and is incapable of arising or existing separate from it. The establishment of a center of life, as in a germ, establishes the first requisite of separate existence.

Diagrammatically the nervous mechanism is a series of cells and protoplasmic threads—polarities, whereby either directly or indirectly every living cell of the animal body is connected with every other cell, and every cell with the body as a whole. The nerve centers, or ganglia, are mechanically the most wonderful devices simplifying the connection of all parts of the body with each other. Large masses of cells are in communication with a series of nerve fibers; these nerve fibers unite in a common trunk; this trunk communicates with a ganglion; other masses of cells similarly related to nerves and to trunk communicate with a ganglion, and the two ganglia are united by a commissure. In this manner the most distant masses of cells are in intimate association, thus securing a certain amount of relatively independent action, yet at the same time capable of joint and harmonious activity. This elaboration of the function of irritability through the nervous mechanism, whereby sensibility is developed in relation to consciousness, does not entirely withdraw the quality of sensitiveness from other tissues. Both living matter and differentiated tissue other than nerve tissue transmit impressions, though in a vague and indeterminate manner. When, however, such impressions reach the nerve tissue, they are brought into definite relations to nerve centers and to consciousness. The first or diffused impressions concern quantity, the second concern quality. The basic impressions caused by heat and cold are very closely allied, and the effect of these on the vitality of a part, when extreme, are the same, producing disintegration and sloughing. The impressions produced by what we call pleasure and pain are also very similar. It requires both consciousness and a nervous system educated by experience to distinguish between such opposite impressions, to say nothing of impressions more closely related. An organized nerve transmits impressions automatically, and directly, without lateral transmission. The ganglia separate, combine and register impressions. In the registry of impressions a similar process may be conceived as occurring as in the formation of nerve tracts, with, however, this difference: in case of nerve formation, polarization implies a direct line of discharge between two points. In the case of ganglionic formation and function the impression returns to the point of beginning, or doubles on itself. These two forms of impressions and structures are related to each other as straight lines are related to circles. There is, however, a still further difference in regard to the fixation of forms. In the fiber the form is comparatively fixed, the tissue of the nerve proper is firm, smooth and glistening. The soft gray matter of the ganglia preserves more or less the spheroidal form, and is therefore less permanently fixed, and admits of frequent re-arrangement of molecules, and re-distribution of impressions. Hence registration of impressions by nerve centers is no more a final act than is the direct transmission of impressions by nerve fibers. The registration of an impression, therefore, involves its transmission to the registering ganglion, as well as the whole series of changes by which it originates, and to which it gives rise. The physical basis of memory therefore cannot be conceived as solely the gray matter of the nerve centers, nor can it be confined to the nervous system, nor to the entire physical body; for these, in part and in whole, in every experience include consciousness as one term of the equation. We could not be conceived as remembering anything of which we are entirely unconscious. On the other hand, it is well to remember that the most painful or the most pleasurable experience, occurring with full consciousness, is not long retained; and that the most of such experiences are in time forgotten. Only consciousness preserves their equivalence.

The nervous mechanism may be diagrammatically represented by the nerve arc. This consists of a peripheral nerve cell with an efferent nerve fiber, a central nerve cell with an efferent nerve fiber terminating in some of the active tissues. This typical form is the mechanical element by the multiplication of which the whole nervous structure is built. These are multiplied and united to form nervous systems.

The entire nervous mechanism divides into two portions, the ganglionic, called also the sympathetic, and the cerebro-spinal. These two portions are brought into direct relation through the ganglia at the roots of the spinal nerves. The sympathetic nervous system is directly related to all the structures and functions of organic life, and indirectly related to the senso-motor and intellectual functions. The cerebro-spinal nervous system is directly related to the senso-motor and intellectual functions, and indirectly related to the functions of organic life. These two structures therefore supplement each other. The sympathetic system is in a general way a center of correlation of lower forms of energy into nervous force; and the cerebro-spinal system is a co-ordinating mechanism securing harmony and equilibrium of the entire organism. In this harmonious order of complex structures and diverse functions the cerebrum presides, and not only exercises final jurisdiction, co-ordinating all other centers, but is also the center of consciousness, though by no means its exclusive seat. Every organized cell is a center of life; every separate organ is relatively a center of consciousness; only the brain is the center of self-consciousness. It is, however, possible to change the center or seat of consciousness by concentration of the will and the exercise of the imagination, and so to place it under other than the usual relations.

We have spoken of the mechanism, the seat, and the center of consciousness, and of the transmission of impressions, as also of the registration of impressions through a redistribution of matter and change in form of arrangement. All these are but the elements through which the varied experiences of life reach consciousness in an orderly manner from the physical side of being. These different parts are defi-

nitely related to the various elements of the phenomenal
world. All phenomena are expressed in terms of matter,
force and motion, and occur in space and in time. Each of
these has a representative sphere and mechanism in the body
of man. The eye through its mechanism and function is
definitely related to space and form, and endows these with
light and color. The ear is a time organ, taking cognizance
of the succession of phenomena, but as there is a point where
light and sound co-ordinate, and as they are definitely related by a common multiple in vibrations, the two organs,
the eye and the ear, have supplementary functions. The
sense of feeling is definitely related to impact, or weight,
and therefore to matter and mass. In the motor apparatus
certain nerves and muscles are concerned with force and
motion. None of these several parts, however, can be disas-
sociated from its fellows any more than we can separate
space and time. The various avenues of the body through
which sensations, perceptions and feelings reach consciousness are many, but consciousness is *one*. There is a provisional center for each group of impressions, and for each
combination of muscles in the senso-motor apparatus, yet
all these provisional centers unite in the seat and center of
consciousness, the cerebrum. It may thus be seen that consciousness is definitely related on the physical side to the
phenomenal world through a complicated mechanism which
is phenomenal in structure and mode of action. Experience
expands this relation and multiplies its details. These various terms concern the relations and manifestations of consciousness, but they do not account for consciousness itself.
It would be indeed foolish to indulge in any speculations as
to the essential nature of consciousness, when we have already acknowledged our entire ignorance of the essence of
so apparently simple a thing as an atom of matter. The
relations and manifestations of consciousness, however, are
very different things; these are as legitimate subjects for
study as are the combinations of matter and the manifesta-

tions of force. Consciousness is related on the one side to
the physical body, evolved in space and time, and existing in
terms of matter, force and motion. Consciousness on the
other side is related to the ideal human form and quality,
involved from the subjective world and existing in the
boundless ocean of ether. Consciousness unites and co-
ordinates these two worlds, epitomized in man, and represented in terms of experience. The development of man
through the intermediation of a center of life and consciousness is therefore a building up of nature and a building down
of spirit. The bodily form is evolved outwardly from the
center, consciousness. The human type is involved toward
the center, consciousness; and coincident with this process
of evolution and involution the area of consciousness in the
individual expands through a twofold experience of the natural and spiritual worlds. Hence we derive an idea of the
relations of individual consciousness to the two worlds of
being. Motive may be conceived as giving color to all these
varied experiences, and motive determines our relations to
truth. Whenever consciousness by its co-ordinate function
in relation to the two worlds has thus created an individual
kingdom in man that apprehends a degree of truth, that is,
has created the two worlds to some extent in man, through
experience of both, the varied colored motives begin to disappear, and give place to the white light of truth. This illumination of consciousness is the dawn of conscience. In
the presence of the light of truth all other motives give way
to the love of truth. The animal *ego,* the selfish motive, recedes. The individual now does right not through fear of
evil, nor from motives of personal gain here or hereafter,
but because truth is in him. There is consonant rhythm in
his soul. He seeks truth, and truth seeks him by a law of
attraction as direct and potent as that which draws the arma-
ture to the magnet, or the needle to the pole. The germ from
which man's bodily life is developed is first a vehicle capable
of being endowed with a distinct personality, and so of be-

coming a separate center of life, and of unfolding higher powers. The act of impregnation fixes upon it the human likeness and sets the wheels of life in motion. Evolution and involution now begin, and development passes through the various lower forms on its way to man. At birth consciousness has developed a center, and a vehicle for a twofold experience, and the center, consciousness, begins to expand into self-consciousness. By the time the child is weaned this development of self-consciousness is well under way, and personal self-consciousness is complete about the seventh year. Then begins the struggle between Good and Evil. The illumination of consciousness, independent action from motive, first of fear and self-interest, and divine consciousness begin to dawn. True, the child very early shows a perception of right and wrong, but such perception is reflected from its surroundings, and not spontaneous. It can be led to believe that it is right to lie and steal, or that it is right to pray and to do right. The child's early experience is taken second-hand from its parents or guardians. It must have liberty to choose, to reject or to select, before it can feel responsibility, and discern motive. All these transitions are by imperceptible gradations. Sometimes these changes come early in life, sometimes late, sometimes not at all. Many adults are deficient in moral responsibility. The defects of birth are many. Heredity gives to personal bias an atmosphere of vice or virtue, in which motive and responsibility breathe and live. The individual, however, has to try all these by experience. If the heredity is good it may have to be adjusted to consciousness through experience. If the heredity is bad it has to be eliminated, and the good created. Many are thus freighted with double loads requiring a lifetime, nay, perhaps many lives to get a fair start. Never till the will to live is subordinated to the will to do good has the individual really begun to live at all in the higher or divine nature.

The physical brain belongs to the phenomenal life of

man. The brain is the organ through which on the one side consciousness manifests outwardly; and on the other side it is the medium through which all sensations and experiences of the outer world are presented to consciousness.

In the objective world phenomena are wrought out on the basis of matter and force, and occur through motion. But beyond all this there are principles and laws by which nature builds, and certain forms or types to which she conforms. Strictly speaking, man invents nothing; he has, however, discovered many things, and all his so-called inventions are but the application of his discoveries of principles and laws in nature to the conditions of the phenomenal world. These laws on the one side, and every possible application of them on the other, already exist in the laboratory of nature. The discovery of laws and the application of principles depend on the accuracy and faithfulness with which man observes and imitates nature. There can nowhere be found a mechanic, a chemist, or a builder like Dame Nature. It is after all the very simplicity of her handiwork that eludes us. Nature knows the secret of perpetual motion, but only as one member of an equation of which the other is eternal rest. In every snow-flake and crystal nature has squared the circle by absolute geometry. Man has never yet been able to utilize more than a fraction of the force everywhere diffused as gravity, heat, light and magnetism. Nature's forms are pure geometry; her compounds are made with absolute exactness; her revolutions are in obedience to immutable laws. Nature alone possesses the secret of the unit of form, the unit of mass, the unit of force, the unit of space, and the unit of time; and she alone knows their common multiple. When man has wrested these secrets from nature then will he indeed be a master-builder. If there is a structure in nature in which all these principles are involved it is the human brain. These principles are represented in, reflected upon, and may be apprehended by the conscious intelligence through the agency of the brain and nervous mechanism. But in order that man may apprehend these principles, the brain must be perfect and consciousness complete. In other words, the structure and function of the brain must reflect the ideal counterpart of the divine man, and consciousness must epitomize the two as one. If now we designate these powers and principles by which nature builds as ideas, thought is their approximate reflection or representation, their partial duplication. What we call human ideas are at best but grotesque and distorted caricatures of divine ideas. Our ideas are imperfect, contradictory, and therefore unstable, like shadows cast by a flickering light upon an ever-varying surface that exists only by virtue of unceasing change. Thought is the evanescent picture, the moving panorama thus produced and presented to a poly-colored consciousness from the nature side of life. Thought is therefore phenomenal like sensation. If we try to control and detain thought, if we endeavor to fix the attention on any one point or on any one thing, we shall realize that it is indeed phenomenal in character. In the very act of controlling it, when successful, we have ceased to think; consciousness has withdrawn to the subjective side of being. Our thoughts come and go and come again, even against our will; they are never twice the same for a single instant, something is lacking, something added, ceaseless change, diversity, instability, unreality. Such is thought. If the external world is thus represented to consciousness, the internal world may also reach consciousness, but not through the physical brain. By thought, generic principles and innate ideas are converted into form by the brain pictures, and thus are nature's laws embodied in a recreative center. The apprehension of these laws and principles in their relations and sequences is the reasoning faculty; but this also involves consciousness. Logical thought differs from illogical thought as a perfect circle differs from an imperfect circle. Thought concerns sensations, ideas, relations and laws, in terms of matter, force, motion, space and time, and represents these to consciousness in terms of experience. Innate ideas are the perfect embodiment of a law of nature with its secondary principles. Our ideas are more or less approximate principles that dimly discern the underlying law of nature. The laws of nature directly relate to pure being beyond all conditions of space and time. Such principles as we discern in nature are the concensus of our varied and, necessarily, fragmentary experience, reproduced in thought and precipitated in consciousness. These innate ideas, laws and principles are derived directly from the subjective world; they are embodied in the phenomenal world; they reach consciousness in man indirectly through experience and bodily feeling, and such experience by a law of attraction furnishes the basis for direct apprehension from the subjective world. To apprehend a law of nature is to have embodied it in our own nature through experience. Hence are derived ideas which are but reflections of innate ideas. Eternity is obscured by time, being beclouded by existence, law producing phenomena, ever present principles lashed into flame by feeling. Man thus colors all he touches and creates an ideal world of his own which has elsewhere no existence, and bends every energy of his will to perpetuate the work of his imagination. Just in proportion as man stands ready to relinquish this selfish world of his imagination for the world of truth and reality, does he come into possession of his birthright in the real world of being. That which everywhere stands in the way of this realization is man's ingrained selfishness, the habiliment of his personality derived from the animal world.

It may thus be seen that thought is the moving panorama of the physical brain, mirroring the world of phenomena. Intuition bears the same relation to consciousness on the spiritual side of being that thought bears to the same consciousness on the material side of existence; but intuition like thought can have no relation to consciousness except through experience. Consciousness stands as the common multiple of both thought and intuition; for consciousness is the sole mediator in man between the natural and spiritual worlds—the bond of union that unites his phenomenal existence in space and time to his real being in the eternal world. Real knowledge is an exact equation between the world of phenomena and the world of being. The terms of this equation are intellect and intuition, with consciousness as the sign of equality. The result of this solution is man's ideal world, the basis of which is his experience of the natural world of effects and the spiritual world of causes. In the *genus homo* man represents the intellect; woman, the intuition. Man reasons, woman feels. Intuition in man represents the female element; reason in woman represents the male element; only the man-woman knows.

Will is the sum of all individual energies; it is that by which he is enabled to focalize these energies on a given point. Will is not mere stubbornness or contrariness. Will wheels the faculties into line and subordinates all minor tendencies to one supreme purpose. It is therefore the polarization of the entire being. This form of concentration of the will is true magic—not witchcraft, or sorcery, or necromancy, but the true *Magus*. It overcomes all obstacles and triumphs in the midst of apparent defeat, and thus accomplishes that which seems impossible. This exercise prolongs life, overcomes disease, and thus triumphs over even death itself. This exercise of the will is impossible so long as man is at war with nature or at war with himself, for he who exercises it must command his passions, appetites, faculties and infirmities, and must conquer even his environment and apparent disabilities. It means first self-conquest, and secondly such a use of his surroundings as will make them tributary to success, where to others without such will they mean defeat and disaster. This is true magic. The handmaid of such a will is imagination. To will thus, one must be able to conceive of that which is beyond the details of his experience, but not beyond his intuitions or the principles of his life. Will and imagination thus rise to the plane of genius. The individual thus endowed is a creator. The conceptions of his imagination, energized by his will, will prove more real and lasting than the things of sense and time. His temporal existence will involve from the world of being, and evolve in knowledge and power. This is but the application of the same principle that has all along enabled us to apprehend the unfolding of man's life on the various planes of existence. We see it here reaching toward higher planes and transcendent powers. To reach this plane requires a strong will, a vivid imagination, the subordination of all lower natures in man, and the inspiration derived from a divine or a diabolical purpose. Just here is the place where two ways meet, and man may become potent for good or evil. Motive now determines all. Either man will become a co-worker with God for the uplifting of mankind, or an embodied evil for man's destruction. The world has witnessed numerous examples of both these types. Here again the motive turns on the principle of egotism or on that of altruism. The animal self of one's own personality is the humane all, through the divine individuality. The Holy Inquisition and the French Revolution illustrate the possibility of incarnate evil; while the list of martyrs rejoicing amid flames, and the unsung heroes and heroines of the cause of truth and righteousness abundantly prove the possibility of the soul's triumph over all its foes. The servants of evil and the servants of truth have often thus stood face to face in the world's history, yet few historians have adequately comprehended the meaning of the situation or the elements involved, because they have written from the planes of self-interest. The glimpses thus revealed of human nature at white heat go to its very foundations, and he who seeks to know himself may thus learn from human kind.

There has been very great progress in recent times, particularly among western nations, in intellectual life and scientific discovery. Two causes have more than others contributed to this result, namely, the discovery and advancement of the art of printing, and the inductive method introduced by Sir Francis Bacon. Nothing can be gained, however, by deceiving ourselves as to the true character of this progress and its bearings on the real interests of man. These discoveries it is true have multiplied our resources and increased our power over nature, but they have in equal measure multiplied our wants. Necessities have given place to luxuries and natural modes of living to artificiality. In the meantime, the religious life of the people has been on the wane, and a puritanical consciousness has been replaced by a widespread covetousness. The race for riches and the lust for political power are fast trampling out the last vestiges of religious obligation. It is true that much of the former religious sentiment was often but another name for superstition, and that in many cases this has given place to enlightenment and reason; but the whole tendency of the times is to do away with all sacred things except perhaps human life and the rights of property; but even here our boasted civilization has generated another class, by no means small or insignificant, with whom the rights of person and property are by no means divine rights, but are held as subservient to so-called communism. In a certain sense this voice of communism is a blind feeling after the humane principle of altruism, engendered by helplessness and envy, and set on fire by the very material power and prosperity to which we have referred. Here again is good and evil face to face; not as heretofore embodied in individuals, but as represented by classes. Neither class is altogether good, nor altogether evil, but each represents a principle. The evil principle of selfish egotism is apparently triumphant, hence its complacence in the face of the gathering storm. Society is thus at war with itself. Capital and labor, the head and the hands of the body politic, are thus in hostile array. The balance of power is really though unconsciously with labor, and it will be a sad day for humanity when the beast in the great unwashed, unfed masses realizes its power and organizes its strength. This terrible realization has been thus far prevented by the humane spirit which has found lodgment and large exercise in the middle class, who are neither rich nor poor, and who are as a rule better read and more charitably inclined than any other class. This middle class include the great bulk of the learned professions, those who mingle intimately with men and women, and who therefore know more of humanity as it is than any other, for this class are taught by that all-potent instructor, human sympathy. To these must be added artisans and the more intelligent and better paid laborers, both men and women. Here is the balance of power, but for which anarchy and desolation would long ago have come to reign. This class know and exercise their power continually. They are foremost in all good works. Drawing their philosophy of life from broad experience, possessed by a humane impulse, this class are the somewhat blind agents of the divine principle of altruism. Clinging to the ancient traditions in the face of intellectual doubt and denial, a contradiction to themselves, they nevertheless feel blindly after the truth and serve it with willing hands. It is indeed true that among the more fortunate few there are many noble exceptions, and the notable increase of large bequests for purposes of charitable relief, and for educational purposes, is an encouraging sign of the times. Yet in the face of all this, the spectacle of a single individual holding in his grasp a hundred millions of money, and of corporations, and trusts, which are able to control legislation and to dictate the terms of trade, the price of food, as well as the compensation for labor, keeps alive the hatred and envy of the starving masses, improvident as they are, and unreasoning as they are likely to remain. Communism will not cure this widespread disease of our boasted civilization, but the spirit of altruism will. Nothing but this spirit in the middle class has been able to hold the disease in abeyance. If the wealth of the world were equally divided among its inhabitants today there would arise tomorrow the distinction of rich and poor, as well as the classes of capital and labor. The divine spirit of altruism lays a heavy hand on greed, and at the same time extends a helping hand to the needy and the ignorant, and even to the slothful and improvident. In the light of a divine humanity the greedy no less than the needy will be benefited by this touch of sympathy that makes the whole world akin. The suffering of poverty may be without crime and is often without envy— not so the embodiment of greed and all uncharitableness. I would plead for these rather than for the hungry poor; they are more to be pitied here and now than any for mere poverty's sake; and the fact that they do not realize their crime only shows how deeply their higher nature has become obscured and degraded. Prosperity often tries the soul of man far more severely than adversity. Opportunities to do good employed for purposes of selfish pride and lust of gain can have but one effect, namely, to degrade and brutalize. On the other hand, adversity is often the alembic that brings out the pure gold of a more noble manhood and womanhood. These are problems that no man can afford to disregard. These principles lie at the very foundation of human nature, and they cannot be ignored without annulling the very foundations of life itself, and setting at naught any rational meaning or possible benefit of individual life on earth. If human life has no higher meaning than animal greed and the survival of the fittest on the plane of the senses, then indeed is man like the beasts that perish. His god is his selfishness, and he had better curse it and die!

To return now from the body politic to the human body, it has been elsewhere shown that the building up of a complex tissue from simple living matter occurs through a process of polarization, tending thus to a fixation of form and definite waves of motion, with ebb and flow of the tide of life from surface to center, and from center to surface. It was also shown how the center of life thus posited becomes also a center of consciousness. This universal tendency to polarization presupposes a universal substance, magnetism, lying back of all forms and beneath all matter. Progressive differentiation of living substance tending to the fixation of form is from first to last a necrosis, or progressive death of living matter. Thus that relative fixation of form with definite function, called muscle, nerve, gland and the like, slowly but surely destroys that mobility and irritability of living matter which specially characterizes unformed protoplasm. Molecular death is therefore the concomitant of life. The endowment of life as a fixed condition belongs to no matter. Progressive endowment of life and progressive death—matter becoming alive, and matter becoming dead—are the conditions of all material substances constituting the animal body or the human form. Here may be seen the principle of death and of rejuvenescence pertaining to the tissues as to the entire body and life of man. In this process of transformation whereby protoplasm takes on the form and function of tissue and organ there is a reserved quantity at any given time of matter endowed with life not thus transformed. This enables the individual to undergo long fasts, and to endure wasting diseases and still recuperate. This reserve of living matter is moreover greatly fortified by the presence of fatty substances rich in carbon, by the oxidation of which the temperature of the body is maintained. This living matter is found in large quantities floating in the bloodvessels and in the lymphatics in which it is specially elaborated. All problems of nutrition relate directly to the formation of these living colloids and their transformation into tissue in the process of growth and repair. In youth the surplus of living matter is large and its transformation rapid. In old age the quantity is relatively small and its transformation slow. In age the form of the tissues has become more fixed; the contour of the body is more angular; polarization pushes the entire bodily organism toward crystallization. The bodily juices dry up, mobility gradually ceases within and without, and molecular death merges into corporeal death, and the matter of life removes to the lower plane of chemism and decomposition.

If now we consider the untransformed living matter of the body *en masse,* the colloids floating in the blood-vessels, lymphatics, and the nuclei of all tissue cells, we shall get the idea of a colloidal body of living matter within the body of tissues and organs. We have frequently referred to the impressibility of the individual colloids of living matter, their sensitiveness to all impressions and their readiness to take on specific forms, and the ease with which they are transformed into tissues having relatively fixed forms. This aggregation of living colloids extending throughout the physical or tissue-body, and anchored in the very center of every microscopic tissue cell, is the only substance to which life directly adheres, and may be conceived as the animal soul, the pure psychic body, the vehicle of sense. This psychic body anchored thus in the center of every living cell constitutes an almost innumerable series of centers of life, dominated by the larger polarities of the body, which polarities are maintained by the circulation of the blood, the circulation being maintained by respiration. Withdraw from any tissue cell the nucleus of living matter and the cell dies. Whenever the body as a whole dies the life departs from the psychic body, but the tissues preserve their form for a considerable time, and the form of the tissues may be artificially preserved for a long time, though every vestige of their function in life departs at death. Even the artificial contraction of muscle under galvanic stimulation is no more than an illustration of a mechanical principle, and a demonstration at best of the principle of magnetic polarization so potent in life. This colloidal psychic body is thus seen as the physical and no less as the vital basis of all organisms, the very web and woof of life, but it cannot of itself determine any bodily form or function. These are impressed upon it from without, or evolved from within. We must not overlook the fact that the first changes in embryonic life begin with this same proteus; nor that the germ, the fertilization of which is the beginning of development, in positing a center of life, contains a nucleus of protoplasm. We must also remember that the earliest manifestation of a developing life center is its power to transform and replenish its store of protoplasm. In a previous section it has been shown that proteus, with its magnetic endowment, or tendency to polarization, lies nearest the ether, and that it readily qualifies in all outward forms of life. The colloidal body then is most directly related to the subjective world. It is that substance which most directly receives all impressions coming from the unseen world of causes and ideal forms. If this psychic or colloidal body may be thus imagined to act as a whole and to receive impressions as any nerve center or sensory area receives them, such impressions have only to be transmitted to consciousness in order to constitute a valid experience. Let us call this function the psychic sense, or direct physico-magnetic impression. All these terms are often used, and in a very illogical and contradictory manner, without any attempt to locate or define them. This psychic body is not the human soul, but the vehicle of the soul, as the tissue-body is the vehicle of the psychic body. We are dealing with material substances and psychic forces, and for the present leaving out of account that great central fact, consciousness, and its next development, self-consciousness, and the relations of these to all physiological and psychological activity. The psychic body bears as definite relations to consciousness in all its forms and degrees on the subjective side of being as does the tissue-body on the objective side; for consciousness stands in the center of these two worlds as represented in man. The psychic body is the reservoir of magnetic power in man. This reservoir has a definite center of its own. This center is manifested as sex. The great solar plexus may be called the sympathetic brain of the psychic body, fortified by the heart and lungs. So far as the physical elements and forces of creative power in man are concerned they are thus located and centered. These furnish the elements of life, but they do not give it ideal form and central endowment. These endowments are subjective, and are involved from higher planes. Sensibility and diffused consciousness belong to the psychic body. It is the vehicle of desire, appetite, lust and passion. Even the lower animals possess in addition to the psychic body a center of life and consciousness, as they are rudimentary-human. Man possesses self-consciousness, as he is rudimentary-divine. We have already shown how as life progresses in concrete degrees the higher nature overtops the lower, and the lower nature still adheres in the higher in the endless chain of existence.

If now we seek illustrations of the psychic sense we are overwhelmed with the magnitude and number of such illustrations. They include the whole body of facts in animal magnetism, taking into account the abeyance and dominance of will and the shifting of consciousness. Cerebral unconsciousness, even when memory is blotted out as by chloroform, leaves the sex-center of the psychic body wide awake and often abnormally active. So also deep sleep that blots out all outward consciousness leaves the psychic center unaffected, and still active. The whole record of experiments in hypnotism is directly related to the psychic body, and even here memory may be impressed independent of ordinary consciousness. The psychic body has a memory and consciousness of its own relatively independent of the brain and self-consciousness. On the other hand the phenomena of clairvoyance and clair-audience, which include consciousness, and are related to the subjective world, are also related to the psychic body and its functions. The bodily avenues of sense are well defined and impressions from the outer world reach consciousness through these, but in rare instances, where these bodily avenues are wanting or obstructed, there is indisputable evidence that impressions from the outer world reach consciousness through other channels. The psychic body as the avenue for subjective impressions now acts also in conveying objective impressions to the sensorium. Even as I write the case of little Helen Keller comes under my notice, through an article by Sallie Joy White in *Wide Awake,* March 1, 1887: "Miss Sullivan began her duties as teacher to little Helen Keller, who, although blind, deaf and dumb, was destined, under her training, to become so great a wonder that scientific men from Europe, as well as this country, would study her as a real intellectual phenomenon.

"Miss Sullivan found her pupil a bright, well-grown girl of nearly seven years of age, with a clear complexion and pretty brown hair. She was quick and graceful, with a merry laugh, and fond of romping with other children. You wonder, don't you, how she can run about and play? Well, she will play *tag,* and have as great a frolic about it as any child you ever saw. She feels the vibrations of the ground by her feet, and so knows just which way to go, and what to avoid. Indeed, her sense of movement is acute, and she tells often about going to church 'to hear the organ play.' She knows when it is being played, in the same way that she can tell which way to run in the game of *tag.* The floor vibrates and thus conveys to her the knowledge of what is being done. It cannot be possible that she gets any real idea of sound in this way, although she must get the rhythmic flow of the music. How much she is able to realize of its beauty and harmony we never will know, but there must be some charm about it, for she is fond of it.

"Would you think that without the ability to hear the music, or to see the steps, she could learn to dance? It doesn't seem possible, does it? And yet she has learned the art; she was taught by one of her little companions. She likes always to do what the other children do, and as they were dancing one day she wanted to join them. The little friend took her hand and tried to make her keep time with her in the step; but she could not manage it. Suddenly, as swift as thought, for with this wonderful child to think and to act are simultaneous, she slid to the floor, and motioning the little girl to go on with her dancing, she felt the motion of her feet and the bending of the knee. In a moment she was on her feet again, dancing merrily; she had caught the spirit of the motion through her little fingers. And now dancing is her favorite diversion.

"It is doubtful whether anyone in possession of eyesight and hearing can arrive at little Helen's acuteness of touch and sensitiveness to motion. We depend on our eyes and ears, and do not call our other senses into full activity, and these other senses will best be studied in persons like little Helen Keller. She can distinguish between puppies of the same litter; and since she has been taught to spell she will spell the name of each one as soon as she touches him. Her sense of smell is so keen that she will recognize different roses by their fragrance, and by the same sense she can separate her own clothes from those which belong to others. She knows if anyone near her is sad. Seldom will physical pain make her cry, but she will discover quickly if a friend is hurt, or ill, or grieved by her conduct, and this knowledge will make her weep bitterly.

"Mr. Anagnos says that her wonderful faculties are matters beyond us. The ideas of death and burial have never been communicated to her; but, when taken into a cemetery, on account of some beautiful flowers there she grew pale and grave, and put her little hands upon her teacher's eyes and her mother's, and spelled out, 'cry, cry,' and her own eyes filled with tears.

"Her teacher says that one day when her brother was coming toward them as they were walking, Helen knew it, spelled his name repeatedly, and started in the right direction to meet him. She gives the names of people she meets walking or riding as soon as their presence is recognized. Often when she is about to make known some plan the child will anticipate her and spell out the plan about to be unfolded. Whether this be the action of some sharpened sense already known to us and named, or the awaking and working of some sense not understood, it is at least an interesting matter for study."

Such cases are by no means uncommon, though the principle under consideration is in the case of Helen Keller illustrated in an unusual degree. To this class belong the Seeress of Prevorst, Heinrich Yung-Stilling, the friend of Goethe, the Drummer Boy of Tedworth, Angelique Cottin, Mollie Fancher of Brooklyn, and thousands of others, all differing in detail of manifestation but not in general principle, thus demonstrating the existence of the psychic sense. It is through this psychic sense that animals are enabled to follow a trail, and the same power has been witnessed in certain human beings, thus showing it to partake of physical qualities capable of transmission to both animate and inanimate objects. Invisible emanations preserving the distinct personal attributes are thus associated with the psychic sense, helping to constitute the psychic body. This psychic body, composed of living matter, anchored in the center of every tissue cell of the human body, and extending thus to every organ and to the utmost bounds of the physical structure, is the medium between the physical structure and the subjective world of ideal forms and all-pervading principles. In the *ovum* the nucleus of living matter receives the impress of the human likeness, and the potential center of life thus posited begins to involve the human form, as it evolves the physical body. The developing germ now passes rapidly and in succession over the various planes of life, marked in the outer world as distinct species. These planes are specially marked by the well-known stages of nutrition, as cell-nutrition, tuft-nutrition, placental nutrition, and finally as mammal nutrition. All this has been referred to in other connections. Here may be noted the broader relations at which we have arrived. The severance of the cord at birth marks the end of placental nutrition, and the wonderful changes in the circulation of the blood that then occur, and the independent respiratory process that then begins, mark an important era in the individual life. The human being rises at once to a higher plane of life. A very careful study of these changes and the just apprehension of their relation to each other and to conscious life will go far toward explaining that great subsequent change called death. The physical body thereafter decomposes, as does the placenta. The incoming and outgoing tide of air is cut off as effectually as is the tide of blood in the umbilical cord. If even as great a change occurs in the latter case as in the former, the vehicle of consciousness shifting now to the subjective plane enters on a new life, as definitely related to the respiratory life as that was to the placental, and as directly to be inferred from the preceding respiratory as that from the placental. The law of analogy is here the great interpreter, discerning from the present both that which has been and that which will be. Consciousness is posited as a center in the center of life of the germ. To this center of life endowed with the fact of consciousness, and impressed with the human form or idea, the waves of involving or evolving force come and go as to a focus. All experience, that is, all sensation and feeling, all motor impressions, the concensus of all bodily changes, are thus focused upon the conscious center of life. This center therefore expands, its channels deepen, as it epitomizes the whole of the unfolding life. The embryo when completely developed is dissevered from its matrix and finally stands alone—a living, conscious, self-centered organism, belonging equally as to fact, but not in degree, to two worlds, the natural and the spiritual, the objective and the subjective. The object is not here to establish or maintain the existence of the human soul, for that must remain with every individual a matter of consciousness to be demonstrated by experience. The object is rather to show the real nature of man as he is, proceeding from a physico-vital plane, and suggest-

ing certain coherent lines of investigation, and certain logical analogies that necessarily arise in our pursuit of truth.
It is true that these methods point in the opposite direction
from spiritual nihilism, and necessitate further analogies,
but these may justly be left to each individual to determine
for himself. What is most urgently needed is a better knowledge of man as he is, here and now, in order that he may
make the very highest and best use of present opportunities.
Other-worldliness often leads to the neglect of these opportunities equally with worldliness. If men and women could
be made to realize that they are here and now living in both
the natural and the spiritual worlds, and if they can be made
to see that through conscious experience they may determine their own position in the scale of being and the helpfulness that they may extend to others, the efficiency of human life will be largely increased. The present object is
therefore to point out these possibilities and to suggest
methods by which they may be realized. To most persons
interested in these studies science is discouraging, philosophy
bewildering, and theology mystifying, and, if they find belief
no longer satisfying, the result is to disarm the individual
of that real zest in life that comes only from a well-defined
purpose enthusiastically pursued. For lack of this zest in
life, apathy settles upon the soul like mildew upon matter,
and eats out its crowning glory. A melancholy pessimist, or
a scoffing materialist, is the result—conditions less desirable
because more demoralizing than blind faith or even ignorant
superstition. These habits of thought are not readily broken
up. The mind may become dissipated and demoralized
through vicious habits of thought, just as the body does
through vicious habits of life. In fact there is no separating
body and mind in this regard. The law of habit equally governs as it underlies both body and mind. We have already
shown that all transmission of energy in a definite direction
tends to the fixation of form, and again that all fixation of
form predetermines the mode of transmission and the form
of energy. All living matter and all living tissue both pos-

sess and transmit energy. The transmission of energy follows the line of least resistance; that is, it goes most readily where it has gone before. The ultimatum is the fixation of specific form, and the transmission of energy—waves of motion—without resistance. The brain is a compound registering ganglion. As age advances registration gradually ceases, and transmission of energy under acquired habit or fixed forms only remains. The physical basis of memory thus finally obliterates memory itself, for as the cerebral habit becomes fixed and precludes all further impression, progressive molecular death, or natural decay obliterates earlier impressions, till finally only the essence of impressions remains as precipitated by experience in consciousness. Finally even consciousness wanes and gives place to senile imbecility. The senso-motor mechanism on the one side bears a definite relation to the psycho-mental on the other. All motions, sensations, feelings and thoughts are definitely related to psychic structure; and any repetition of impulse in any of these lines of experience tends to diminish resistance, and to facilitate very greatly a repetition of the similar impulse, or in other words, to establish the habit. The range of activities that may thus become automatic is very great. Acts performed at first with difficulty, with concentration of mind, and with energy of will, are not only finally performed without effort, but are performed unconsciously, and while the mind is concentrated on other things. What may be called natural organic volition is now supplemented by acquired or artificial volition. In the exercise of muscle, which up to a certain point promotes development, there is a definite relation between force and mass, between energy and resistance. In the more delicate muscular manipulations requiring a wide range of activities, differentiation still tends to automatism. Automatism is therefore directly related to differentiation, and inversely related to mass. The cessation of the process of differentiation is the fixation of habit. We have now derived the elements with which to determine the laws of habit in regard to mental processes. The building up of the brain structure and the exercise of its normal function have their root in the general principles of physiology. The form of tissue, the relations of parts, and the method of action are determined by the laws of mathematics, thus determining both symmetry and harmony. This complex structure, the human brain, like all other tissues, is in constant need of rejuvenescence, and hence both normal and abnormal forms are repeated and perpetuated. A normally-developed healthy brain has within itself, and through its natural exercise, a power and perpetuity but little known and seldom seen. On the other hand, just as a bridge or building erected in disregard of the principles of mechanics —weight, tension and the strength of material—contains within itself the elements of its own destruction beyond the encroachments of time and natural decay, and is liable to fall at any time by its own weight, or by a slight strain such as a well-constructed edifice could bear with safety; so it is with that vital mechanism, the human brain. Evil thoughts and all vicious mental states overcome resistance, and mold the structure till it repeats automatically the evil, as it repeats the good impulse. Every evil impulse thus repeated tends from the first to disharmony and to disease of the entire structure, and finally results in ruin. It is physiologically true, that "the wages of sin is death." The law of habit has its root in the anatomy of the body, of which the brain is a part; its motor power is in the physiology of nutrition and circulation; its theater of activity is in the protean living matter; the principle of its activity lies in polarization; its forms and relations are in the principles of mathematics, and the key to its interpretation is analogy.

As we ascend from the general psychological plane toward the center of being we encounter two principles, namely, will and desire. Will is to the mind what vitality is to the body, namely, the sum of all its energy. Desire is the directing agency of mind and body, as appetite or hunger is the directing agency of the vital body. What we call motive gives color to will, desire and appetite, as it relates all these to results and to other individuals. Motive is therefore related to self-consciousness, the attribute of the reasoning mind. Consider, for example, that manifestation of desire known as lust. Desire through the imagination pictures to the mind, and through vitality inflames the blood in anticipation of the coveted enjoyment. The will is chained to vitality, self-consciousness is obscured, and mere psychic sense is centered in the sexual center of life. Thus the animal *ego* reigns supreme. With every repetition of this allegiance to lust resistance decreases, and the imagination revels in its new creation till the habit of both mind and body conform to the animal ideal. Many persons fail to distinguish between this passion and love. These two principles have not only nothing in common, but they are the direct antipodes of each other. Lust seeks all for self, and mercilessly devours. Love is beneficent, and seeks another's good. In seeking all for self, lust not only destroys its victims and destroys itself, but destroys its possessor. There is a road by which human beings may lose their humanity and descend, body and soul, to the plane of the brutes. Consciousness descends from the higher self, to the sex-center of the psychic body or animal soul, and our hospitals and insane asylums are filled with these victims of lust, where insanity, imbecility and drivelling idiocy protest in the name of humanity at the disregard of nature's plainest laws. Those who really know human nature through any wide experience directed by sincere desire for the truth know that, upon a correct knowledge of the meaning of sex, and the true relations of the sexes, depend the happiness and well-being of the human race, more than upon anything else in its present stage of development. And yet those who have learned the truth in these regards cannot reveal it because of the predominance in the great bulk of humanity of the animal *ego* over the divinely human, the triumph of the selfish over the humane, of lust over love. The larger liberty and prophetic enfranchisement of woman can only redeem the human race and lift even man himself into his divine birthright. The pure love nature is strong in every true woman, and she will thus render good for evil in measure altogether divine. Here lies the secret of happy homes, of healthy and healthful human beings, of divinely inspired human souls. Love is but another name for that spirit of altruism which rises above the animal plane, and enables human beings to conquer self and give place to the divine. This is the one principle that in all its varied applications elevates man above the brute. Animal egotism has deluged the world with blood in the name of ambition, which is lust for power. Animal egotism has trampled down the finer sensibilities of the soul in its lust for fame. Animal egotism has filled the world with poverty and woe in its lust for gold; and animal egotism has degraded woman in every age under the sacred name of love; and the great mass of mankind has yet to learn this lesson: "He alone can truly possess the pleasure of love who has conquered the love of pleasure."

One law underlies the entire nature of man; it is the universal law of duality, and its final expression in human beings is sex in its highest and purest relations, under the divine inspiration of love. Under this law the growth of altruism, where the lower powers of man's nature are subordinated to the higher, tends to self-preservation, health, happiness, and long life, and beyond all this it lays the foundation for the unfolding of still higher faculties in man, as well as for his final supreme enlightenment as a spiritual being evolved from the human plane. The disobedience of this higher law, where man's higher powers are subordinated to the animal passions, inevitably tends to disease and death. We cannot fail from these considerations to deduce a physical basis for a natural code of moral ethics, justified by every known principle of physiological science and fortified by the lessons of experience. The human body and the laws of life thus contain a divine revelation in perfect accord with that other revelation which declares that the "wages of sin is death," and that righteousness hath the gift of life forever more.

CHAPTER XI.

The *terra incognita* of modern physical science is consciousness. This fact is often realized, but instead of going
seriously to work to study the relations and different states
and conditions of consciousness, the foolish attempt is repeated again and again of trying to fit consciousness to
phenomena as an attribute of matter. Whenever the changes
arising in the conditions and manifestations of consciousness
have been carefully noted and critically compared, such observation and comparison have led to the conclusion that
consciousness is the prime factor in all individual experience, and by no means confined to the senso-motor mechanism of the human brain. It is true that in one of its modes
consciousness bears a definite relation to the brain and all
mental processes that directly relate to the external world of
phenomena. In moments of so-called abstraction, when, as
often occurs, the individual is in a deep study, the phenomenal world is largely shut off from consciousness; the physical senses are dormant, and in this condition the individual
enters the border-land of an ideal world. All great artists,
poets and painters who possess real genius thus derive their
inspirations. These, however, usually get but glimpses of the
real world of ideal forms and all-pervading principles, yet
enough oftentimes to immortalize their names. The bodily
avenues between the external world and consciousness are
many. Consciousness is *one*. Consciousness therefore is
the vehicle of the *ego*. In its existence consciousness may
be independent of all bodily sense or mental condition,

though dependent on these for its external manifestation. Through these avenues and relations the conscious *ego* comes into definite relations to a phenomenal existence, to the things of sense and time; and by analogy something may be inferred of the nature of consciousness from its outward manifestation. When once it is understood, however, that through its relations to the brain and sensory ganglia consciousness manifests in but one of numerous forms, analogies drawn from this one form alone will no longer be regarded as final, even where they are logically so drawn. Complete self-consciousness on any plane is impossible except where the higher faculties in man control the lower. Until this condition is achieved the *ego* can control neither the thoughts nor the acts of its complex environment. In other words, complete self-consciousness implies complete self-control. The individual is then enabled to concentrate the mind upon a given object and to exclude all others. Whenever this condition is fairly approximated the individual has already learned that there are other states of consciousness, and can begin to enter them at will. The range of individual experience which has elsewhere been shown to be the basis of all knowledge is thus broadened immensely, and even the nature and value of ordinary experience on the physical plane can now for the first time be estimated, because it is brought into relations of comparison with experience on other planes. It may thus be seen how important is the relation that consciousness bears to the bodily mechanism, and how unwise it is to mistake the varying mental states occurring under one form of consciousness for the variation in the modes of consciousness itself, with some of which the mind, as a function of the physical brain, has little if anything to do. It has more than once been shown in these pages that consciousness is not only the central fact in man, but that it is thus the medium between the objective and subjective worlds. If this be true, then consciousness is on one side related to the universal ether from which proceed all ideal forms, and in which are precipitated all created things, the essence of these thus returning to the original source whence they emanated. Newton's phrase, *Sensorium Dei,* the organ of divine consciousness, as applied to the ether, thus becomes intelligible. The importance of the conception that consciousness on the one side is as definitely and as naturally related to this "organ of divine consciousness" as on the other side it is related to the things of sense and time cannot be overlooked; for such a concept goes far toward explaining the nature of man and his true relations to existence. There is nothing more remarkable in the conceptions of man today than the fact that he generally supposes that his life proceeds outwardly only, on the physical plane, and that his thoughts and reflections concern only those outward experiences. It is as though man stood with his back to a blank wall and his whole nature and life proceeded thence in one direction. True it is that he recognizes vague thoughts and intense longings regarding the beyond, and his imagination pictures the habitations of the blessed with palm trees and crystal streams flowing from delectable mountains, but these are but reflections of earth-life divested of sorrow and pain and yet conditioned in sense and time. When once it is clearly seen that the brain and the whole process of thought, together with the avenues of sense, are the relations of consciousness to the outer world alone, and that not thought, but consciousness is the prime factor in individual life, then the blank wall disappears, and the undiscovered country looms up before us, obscured by clouds and mists, but no longer an undiscovered world, though still unexplored. If instead of jumping the gulf between the present and the future, and discussing the immortality of the soul, man would carefully consider the question as to whether he has a soul, and its nature and conditions here and now, a great step would be gained, not only in knowledge of the soul, but as to the conditions of its growth and enlightenment. This knowledge will dawn upon the human understanding just in proportion as man is enabled to apprehend the relations and manifestations of consciousness. Whenever it is clearly recognized that all our knowledge comes by experience, and whenever the relations of the external world through these experiences are clearly discerned, it will also be discovered that we are conscious of experiences beyond the phenomenal world of sense and time, and independent of the sensory ganglia and the thinking brain. This line of investigation will render clearly apprehensible the existence of a supra-sensible or subjective world of being. Judging then by the nature and relations, rather than by the extent of our subjective experiences, we shall be able logically to arrive at the further conclusion that, from the very nature of things, this subjective world is the very counterpart of the objective world of sense and time. We shall next be able to locate consciousness as related to these two worlds, and thus to locate our two sets of experiences, and to make one set a test of the other through the laws of analogy and correspondence. By this time we shall have discovered that we have actually begun the exploration of the undiscovered realm, and placed it beyond the possibility of time and sense to reconstruct for us the old stone wall at our backs. Man may thus begin to know himself. Suppose that it be assumed that man has an immortal soul that still lives beyond the bounds of time; that indeed is not the all-important question. Suppose that the soul lives hereafter, but that memory is blotted out, and that we have there no recollection of anything that occurred to us here. This would practically be annihilation. The old *ego* in its new form would be for us a new creation, and *we* would be blotted out. It is a matter of common experience that memory fails us. The events of yesterday not only are forgotten today, but there comes a time in the encroachment of age when all records of past events are blotted out, and when new impressions are well-nigh impossible. Consciousness, and not memory, is the human factor that remains, even in the face of senile imbecility. Again admitting the continuance of the individual soul beyond the gates of death, the prime question is: Will it preserve self-consciousness? Suppose now that we have discovered the fact of consciousness on the subjective plane while in this present life, and while inhabiting a physical body. If we have clearly apprehended the fact that consciousness is the immediate vehicle of the individual *ego,* and that thought is only the channel of communication between consciousness and the external world, and if we have discovered that consciousness depends on thought, and brain, and sense, and muscle, for its external manifestation, but not for its existence, we are already in the way of determining both the fact and the conditions of manifestation of another form of consciousness from that of objective life. Putting the problem in this form the unknown is not necessarily the unknowable; the undiscovered is not necessarily the undiscoverable. The measure of man's existence on the earthly plane of life is determined by his experience on that plane; but if the conscious center of man's life is posited at the center between two worlds and naturally open to both, then it follows that at any time the measure of his existence on the subjective plane is also determined by his experience on that plane. If the cycle of experience of the conscious *ego* be rounded up by wide and co-ordinate experience on both planes, consciousness may be imagined to grasp not only greater depths, but to approximate even the details of experience, and so to approximate what we understand as memory. On the other hand, if one's experience here concerns almost exclusively the objective plane, if the life of the individual is immersed in sense, and anchored to self, thus ignoring divine altruism and the voice of the higher self, it must be seen to pertain to the things that perish, and which do not follow the ego after the death of the body to the subjective plane. If again we imagine the cycle of experience to be rounded up, the *ego* would be left in darkness, there could be no self-consciousness on the subjective plane, self-consciousness having displayed itself previously so largely in the things that no longer exist. If these analogies of consciousness be correctly drawn, they serve to explain why, if the doctrine of re-incarnation be true, no memory of past lives is retained by the *ego* after the lapse of ages and repeated incarnations, the ego having shifted from plane to plane. The extent in which this doctrine of re-incarnation has been held in all ages down to the present time, and even by the fathers and later dignitaries of the Christian church is generally overlooked. We are at present, however, concerned only with the present life, and the logical analogies of present experience. These questions are in no sense transcendental, but are the most practical and sensible that the human mind can suggest, and more than all others concern the present life and the best interests of man. The doctrine of rewards and punishments is but a childish and superstitious view of the divine principle of justice, that metes to every one according to the deeds done in the body, according to the thoughts of the mind, and the ideals that inspire the individual life. Justice is that silent but all-potent law that veins the leaf and crystallizes the snow-flake by exact measure and perfect equilibrium. "The wicked obey the law through fear; the wise keep the law through knowledge." One may be poor and despised by the world, without fame or power, yet if his soul be open to the voice of the needy and the cry of distress, if his life be unselfish and he be considerate toward others, he is rich indeed. He may be indifferent as to either food or raiment and yet be clean both within and without. He may have little to give, and yet be helpful and inspiring, and blessings may follow his footsteps like his own shadow on a summer day. Such an one is in the world, but not of it. He is conscious of the subjective plane of being, and his experience extends to the other world even while in the body. The *ego* enthroned in his consciousness is lifted to serener heights, and for him there is no undiscovered clime. Of old it was written: "He that is dead to the world is alive to God." Nothing so bars the soul from the subjective world as selfishness. The thoroughly selfish person is like a blind horse in a bark-mill; his experience and his vision are hedged about by his narrow circle, and he wears continually the channels of self deeper at every round. This is not a mere matter of sentiment, nor is it merely a matter of religion which so many now-a-days treat with scorn; it is a matter as directly determined by physiological law as is the beating of the heart, or the development and function of the brain.

Individuals are born with widely different natural endowments. Education cannot repair the defects of birth, but the determined effort of the will of the individual cannot only repair these defects, but it can take advantage of every hereditary trait, whether good or bad, and transform it to use and beneficence. There are three conditions of consciousness in ordinary daily experience: that of ordinary wakefulness, that of dreamful sleep, and that of dreamless sleep. We have already shown that not memory but consciousness is the all-potent factor in man. Consciousness as a fact returns to the individual, as well as memory, after deep sleep. Everyone will admit that in sleep, where dreams occur, consciousness is on a different plane, or under different conditions from the waking state, and memory brings into the waking state the subject and the varied experiences of dreams. After dreamless sleep memory may bring nothing back from the subjective world, but it resumes the thread of life just where it was dropped before unconsciousness came on. Now what becomes of consciousness during dreamless slumber? Either it continues or it does not. If it continues then it must simply be on another plane and under different conditions, at least so far as thought and memory are concerned, for the gap is between consciousness and memory in relation to thought. If on the other hand consciousness is blotted out and re-created every time we enter dreamless sleep, it could not be that both consciousness and memory, both new creations, at once take up the thread of life just where they dropped it, and resume the even tenor of their way as though nothing had happened. Nature never does things in that way. Her adjustments require time, her developments and all her varied relations are slow growths. Both consciousness and memory have grown and expanded from the original germ. The true philosophy of dreams is then a problem in the conditions of consciousness, while we may fairly assume that consciousness still persists in dreamless sleep, though under changed conditions. Nothing is more common in ordinary life than the shifting of the planes of consciousness. Take for example the action of anæsthetics, chloroform changes the consciousness of the real *ego.* The individual cannot be called strictly unconscious. He is not conscious in the ordinary way. He suffers no pain, and retains no recollection of what occurs while under the influence of the anæsthetic, but the organic consciousness remains undisturbed. Muscular motion may occur, but without co-ordination. The cerebrum, cerebellum and sensory ganglia are unconscious in dreamless sleep; the medulla, spinal cord, solar-plexus and the sexual-area are wide awake and sometimes these are super-sensitive. The light of self-consciousness is withdrawn; it is drawn within, but not quenched. In syncope consciousness is withdrawn; but if one will watch carefully the first returning consciousness it will generally be found that it has been by no means dead or idle, for by gently attracting the individual's attention in the dawn of returning consciousness, after a faint, it will be found that a few seconds have sufficed for the recovery of a long-forgotten experience, restored again from the all-surrounding, all-pervading ether. These few seconds of suspended animation are often sufficient for the weaving of a romance, or for the enactment of a tragedy, and such experiences are not always fantastic and unreal, as experience and observation prove. But perhaps the common instances of somnambulism or sleep-walking offer the best demonstrations of double consciousness. Persons subject to these attacks really lead double lives. Individuals walking in their sleep have been known to appear among strangers, enter into conversation, and yet in the ordinary waking state retain no recollection of the events or persons. On the succeeding night, however, walking again, the previous night's experience has been recovered and continued. Even one such case is sufficient to show a natural division in consciousness, and a gap occurring between them so far as memory is concerned. The experiments in magnetism, and more especially the recent hypnotic experiments give similar results. In many of these cases the knowledge possessed by the individual in the subjective state altogether transcends that of objective consciousness. Such persons have been known to diagnose correctly their own diseases and to determine the duration and termination of the same. Until a very recent date the majority of so-called scientists have shown a disposition to ignore or ridicule such cases, in spite of their overwhelming authenticity, and now when they seem inclined to investigate these phenomena they learn that they are not produced at the will of the subject, nor do they readily come under the will of those who are entirely ignorant of the laws under which they occur. The wiser method is to ignore nothing that concerns human nature and to take advantage of every opportunity to investigate, and particularly to examine unusual phenomena. In the delirium of fevers, and in the intoxication produced by alcohol and various drugs, there is a shifting of the planes of consciousness and consequent aberration of memory. With the insane consciousness is permanently disturbed, and such cases are best studied as aberrations of consciousness. It may be doubted whether such a thing as unconscious cerebration ever occurs, though there may be mental processes either above or below the plane of memory. To assign all mental aberrations to the imagination, as though thereby explained, is to mistake the office of both imagination and consciousness.

In the delirium caused by opium and alcohol, consciousness is shifted to a subjective plane, and sometimes to a very low plane. It is a great mistake to assume that the objects seen and the events that occur have no real existence. If all these are to be regarded as the creations of the imagination, we are at a loss how to explain the great uniformity of the objects witnessed from the effect of alcohol, for example. When we get any rational idea of the subjective world we shall discover that the snakes and dragons seen there are as veritable on that plane, to subjective sense, as their living prototypes are on the phenomenal plane to objective sense, for it must be remembered that the universal ether is that infinite ocean whence all creation proceeds, and into whose all-dissolving bosom all things return. Our relation to objects here is largely incidental, determined by location, circumstance and the like. On the subjective plane our relations are determined by attractions and intrinsic conditions, and an individual full of all evil passion, inflamed by alcohol, will attract entities of like degree, and so on to the end of the list. To say that all such cases result from pure imagination is by no means to explain them. Many persons assume that when they have named a thing they have explained it, and that further questions are an impertinence. Perhaps the most important consideration in regard to the shifting states of consciousness from the objective to the subjective condition regards that vague and varying state known as insanity. As a rule with the insane this transfer of consciousness is partial, seldom complete. Consciousness is rather out of joint than actually transferred from plane to plane. There is usually an organic lesion, or a functional obstruction that tends to tissue change in some of the nerve centers. The result in many cases is to break down that sharp line of demarkation between the objective and subjective worlds. The individual becomes bewildered, loses his bearings; his experiences are no longer co-ordinate. The instrument through which consciousness is manifested is out of tune, and the result is discord. In regard to these cases of perverted function it is a mistake to think that no differentiation is made as to the planes or states of consciousness; practically but one state of consciousness is recognized. The further mistake is made of looking upon all objects cognized, and upon all experiences outside of the ordinary plane of consciousness, as altogether non-existent; that is, a figment of the imagination. But what is imagination? Let us ask the artist, the poet, the painter, ask genius that is so closely allied to insanity, ask all who create from ideal forms, and they will tell us, one and all, that imagination is the wings of the soul that bear up the lagging fancy, the slow and plodding mind, till it enters the ideal world and gazes there on both beauty and deformity in all their nakedness. They will tell us that what we call the real world is at best but a poor and colorless caricature as compared with the ideals open to the imagination, and that what is generally termed the work of genius, bears but a touch of that transcendent truth and reality that veils its face from every faculty of man on the phenomenal plane. Let us ask the true scientist what we know of anything, of matter, space, time, or motion, of the whole phenomenal world, and he will tell us, and tell us truly, that we have *our own ideas* of these, and nothing more. Finally, ask that greatest of modern philosophers, Schopenhauer, what imagination is. He will tell us that not only the world, but ourselves included, are reducible to two terms, imagination and will. The one is the essence and the creator of all forms in nature; the other, the motive and creative power, and these powers are as potent on the subjective as on the objective plane; they are as active in drunken delirium, and in insanity, as in that other condition of consciousness that we call sanity. If in the phenomenal world we build toward our ideals, we seldom realize them. All that we thus build not only fails to come up to our ideals, but they have incorporated into their entire structure both disappointment and decay, from turret to foundation stone. It may thus be seen that imagination is a potent factor on every plane on which consciousness holds open court, and that our ideas are often less realities on the phenomenal plane of outer sense than on any other. The amount of empirical evidence demonstrating the existence of the subjective plane is simply overwhelming, and these facts have been quite long enough regarded as mere coincidences. They are, indeed, often accidents of birth, temperament, disease and the like, so far as any human quality or human experience can be regarded as accidental. These irrelevant and spasmodic experiences are often a source of great distress, and even of calamity to the individual, disqualifying him for the life of the world while yet unfitted to realize and utilize these potent factors in the subjective life. Whenever scientists, so-called, are tired of the supreme folly of trying to deduce consciousness from matter, and of ignoring the plainest facts in everyday experience, and whenever they will go seriously to work by both induction and deduction to investigate consciousness in all its manifestations and relations, they will have entered on a line of research that will very soon astonish them. Why, it may be asked, have scientific men as a whole made so little headway either in investigating that psychological babel, modern spiritualism, or in staying its progress even among the educated and intelligent? I answer unhesitatingly, because they have with few exceptions contented themselves with parrot-like reiteration of a meaningless phrase, *unconscious cerebration;* and then they have smiled in each other's faces over the humbuggery of assuming that they know what their slogan means. They have gone further than this. They have put forth this thimble-rigging psychology as orthodox science, and done their best to taboo everyone who dared to question their conclusions and investigate for himself. The announcement has again and again been made that *now* science is going to take up the subject and handle it as only scientists can. But alas! for those who have waited with great expectations for the results! These wiseacres have like children been frightened by their own bug-a-boo. Some one would impeach their orthodoxy and it would ruin their prospects as pure scientists. Does this all sound like a tirade? Then *examine the records,* from the times of Mesmer and Von Reichenbach down to Hodgeson's report. It is no excuse to say that the whole subject is mixed with fraud, uncanny and not altogether respectable. Say what you please of this psychological babel, it spreads over the globe. Noted mediums are invited to the palaces of princes, and there is more table-tipping and spirit-communion on the sly than spirit-drinking at the tables of the rich. So-called mediumship is often a disease with an almost irresistible tendency to suicide, and it is often as contagious as the epidemic monomania of the sixteenth century. Scientific denunciation has been as powerless to stay the spread of spiritualism as *unconscious cerebration* to explain it. True science apprehends a real cause behind every phenomenon of nature, and even delusion and monomania are no exceptions. If scientific men would but recognize the fact of subjective consciousness that is demonstrated every time they sleep, or give chloroform, or hypnotize an individual, nay, every time a weak woman faints in a crowded room, and then go to work in earnest to arrange and classify all facts derived from this plane of life, they would presently be able to offer such an explanation of the powers and planes of action of individual consciousness as would dissipate the delusions and diminish the dangers of dealing with the dead. That our individual consciousness, which in one of its states is related to the outer phenomenal world, is on another plane independent of space and time, as we understand these terms, is a matter of easy demonstration; and it offers an explanation, when once clearly defined and understood, of a great deal of undeniable human experience now attributed to ghosts and goblins damned. Having determined what experiences are genuine, which is often exceedingly difficult, a better knowledge of the powers of man and of his states of consciousness will assign to the embodied soul on earth the greater part of the spiritualistic phenomena. If one were to point out the dangers of these attempts to deal with the dead, he would be met by anger and scorn. It is the most useless and dangerous form of other-worldliness. It draws the attention from present duty and possibilities in the present life, and reverses the only method by which either any individual, or the race as a whole, has ever risen in the scale of being. The whole effort of spiritualism would seem to be to determine and to force the return of a disembodied soul to earthly consciousness, and to drag it back into matter; while every thoughtful person ought to be aware that the elevation of man depends on the degree in which he rises toward the spiritual world. The time will doubtless come when the so-called materializations will be better understood, and every clean person will avoid them then, as the more enlightened among the spiritualists do now. Admitting, for the sake of the argument, the whole philosophy and phenomena of modern spiritualism, these efforts to drag the soul back to earth and down into matter can justly be compared to criminal abortion, where the embryo is wrenched from its normal environment by an impulse akin to murder, the fitting handmaid of animal lust. These twin abominations require a third member to constitute an unholy trinity that shall be a fit companion for Cerberus, the three-headed dog that guards the gates of the infernal regions, and these dealings with the dead may furnish the missing member. This may be strong language, but it may be found hereafter that the blood of the slaughtered innocents that so continually cries to heaven in this our boasted civilization will vie with these dealings with the dead in barring the gates of paradise to those who have so thwarted the will of nature and disregarded her plainest laws. Dynamite destroys regardless of the ignorance of him who unwisely trifles with it. One world at a time is quite enough for the best of people to deal with, and the best of people have in all time earned that title by their efforts to elevate the human race on earth, and to ameliorate the condition of humanity; no other world can be anticipated without neglect of this.

What we need is to know more of man as he is here and now, and this knowledge will never be derived from psychological jugglery. Such explanations as are to be derived from psychological laws have now been so long delayed that otherwise intelligent persons convinced beyond all cavil of the truth of many experiences and phenomena of so-called spiritualism are ready to denounce any other than the orthodox explanations of the spiritualists as direct dealings with the dead. These persons have come to their present conclusions by long and patient trial, with great hesitancy, and often only after repeated disappointments from so-called science; and having at last despaired of any other explanation than that which spiritualism offers they have come to the conclusion that none other exists. The responsibility here lies at the door of science. It is her sin of omission, and she should hasten to correct it. The subjective plane of being is to be subjectively experienced, and when such subjective experience is that of another, and not our own, it is no more evidence for us than any other matter taken on faith in the intergity and intelligence of an observer. In cases where supposed materializations from the subjective world occur, the most simple and at the same time the most comprehensive fact is generally overlooked, namely, that all that appears, all that is material and visible to the objective sense, is not spirit, not subjective; and granting that the phenomenon is genuine, it is no evidence of spirit life or individual identity. What the thing was before being materialized, and what it will be afterward, is as unknown to us as before. Admitting all that is claimed for the phenomenon, the explanation is not conclusive, nor is it the only one possible. The most wonderful materialization is man himself, and our opportunities to investigate him are all that could be desired. We are not confined to dark seance-rooms, a stifling atmosphere, and doomed to have both hands held fast lest we should touch or see our subject under investigation. We can examine our subject at high noon, in the broad light of day, at midnight when slumber closes his eyelids and all external consciousness is withdrawn, and when the flitting pictures of dreams mold his outer life to expressions of emotion. We can examine him in the palace and in the hovel, under every stress of feeling, and rocked like a frail vessel with surging passion. Here is a materialized spirit if there is one anywhere, and yet man turns from him, from his own embodied consciousness, and hunts for ghosts and ghouls. We neglect the offices of kindness and the words of love and helpfulness till our friend is snatched beyond the veil, and then devote the rest of our lives to knocking at the door through which he passed to inquire if he still lives and is happy! Alas! the irony of life in the presence of the mystery of death! Alas! the hypocrisy over death in the presence of the mystery and the wasted opportunities of life!

"I wage not any feud with Death
  For changes wrought on form and face;
  No lower life, that earth's embrace
May breed with him, can fright my faith.

*   *   *   *   *   *   *

"Eternal process moving on,
  From state to state the spirit walks;
  And these are but the shattered stalks,
Or ruined chrysalis of one.

"How pure at heart and sound in head,
  With what divine affections bold,
  Should be the man whose thoughts would hold
An hour's communion with the dead.

"In vain shalt thou, or any call
  The spirits from their golden day,
    Except, like them, thou too canst **say,**
My spirit is at peace with all."

CHAPTER XII.

The most earnest and the most able students of the phenomena of nature have often been led to the conception that all the forces in nature that manifest their presence as special modes of motion are resolvable into one force, and that this one force is the latent energy lying back of all phenomena. It has been elsewhere suggested in these pages that what we recognize as magnetism answers more nearly to this universal force than any form of energy known to us today. To say that magnetism is life would be a meaningless assertion in the present condition of our knowledge of either life or magnetism; and yet the phenomena of life and the phenomena of magnetism are very closely related to each other. Life, like magnetism, seems to be everywhere diffused. Each seems ready to manifest its presence on the slightest provocation, the conditions of their manifestation so far as we know being very simple, yet the conditions are very different in the two cases. No life dissociated from organisms is manifest to us. Magnetism on the other hand manifests its presence in both animate and inanimate nature, and no radical difference has yet been discovered between animal and terrestrial magnetism. It might logically be conceived that magnetism is that latent energy everywhere diffused in nature, which, under certain conditions, assumes the special mode of motion designated as heat, light, electricity and the like, and which at the same time constitutes the sum of that energy of the organism called vitality. The vital phenomena of organisms are manifest in

(184)

a great variety of forms, and may be conceived as involving and combining all other modes of motion, and at the same time there are still higher forms of energy displayed by organisms that are found nowhere else in nature. If magnetism and life cannot be conceived as synonyms, magnetism and vitality may be found more closely allied, though life is more than mere vitality, and vitality is more than magnetism. It should be borne in mind that we do not know the essence of any force, no matter how simple its display, and it should also be remembered that the energy of living beings is directly related to that which alone manifests life, namely, the organism. While therefore we may consider life in its relation to mere vitality and to magnetism on the one side, we must not forget that life bears a definite relation to all special modes of motion, and variations of structure designated as organic on the other side; or, we must remember the structure and conditions of manifestation while considering the energy that is displayed. Again, it should be remembered that magnetism in organisms is the polarizing agency, and that while it determines organization, facilitates movement, and co-ordinate rhythm, it tends also to the fixation of form which in the end crystallizes and destroys. In other words, the motive power of life is at last a consuming fire. So far as dynamics are concerned, the creator and the destroyer are one.

"Life evermore is fed by death,
    In earth, and sea, and sky;
And, that a rose may breathe its breath,
    Something must die.

"From lowly woe springs lordly joy;
    From humbler good, diviner;
The greater life must aye destroy
    And drink the minor."

It may thus be seen that both life and vitality are something more than magnetism. The most comprehensive fact in germ or organism is not mere vitality, not the quantity of force present, nor yet the fact that this energy manifests a great variety of movements. The most comprehensive fact is *the positing of a center of life, and the unfolding of a still interior center of consciousness.* The principle of form and order, the laws of development, and the mode of action, transcend the mere equivalents of energy. It is true that no life is manifest without movement of matter, and that vitality represents both the motive power and the sum of all energy, and magnetism may be the source whence vitality is derived; but, if this were all, then a steam engine and a block of stone would be of equal value as motors when inspired by steam.

No adequate idea of the real meaning of the word health is possible except in intimate relation with the word life; and no adequate conception of the meaning of the word life is possible dissociated from an organism, which alone manifests life. Life is something more than any or all force, and health is something beyond all energy or mere vitality. If no amount of mere vitality alone constitutes life, so no mere lack of energy can alone cause disease or death. Neither life, nor health, nor disease can be regarded as mere kinematics.

When we regard life as an endowment of matter, even in the relatively formless matter called protoplasm, we find it always associated with an organism, so that the foregoing principles hold good even here. Previous to the positing of a center of life, and the building of an organism, we cannot conceive of life as being manifested in matter, or in any sense as an attribute of matter alone. If, therefore, life can be said to be in any sense an attribute of matter, even of protoplasm, so in the same sense, though perhaps in a less degree, can life be predicated of all matter—latent in one case, and manifest in another. Whenever so-called living matter has been analyzed no element has been found unfamiliar to the chemist. We may regard the life principle, or the potency of life, as diffused everywhere in nature, and all matter as waiting for the manifestation of life. A considerable portion of the matter of the globe has no doubt thus been at one time involved in the manifestation of life, and these remains of organisms constitute alike the ocean's bed and the mountain's mass.

So far as life can be regarded as a quality of matter it is everywhere one in kind. There is, indeed, one flesh of beasts, another of fishes, another of birds, and another of man; but the life principle in all these is not many, but one. The matter of life in all these varied forms is convertible, one into the other, and such conversion modifies the organism that feeds on other forms of life, though this alone cannot change the nature of beast or man.

If life as a quality of matter is everywhere the same in kind, we may define health in any case, whether in plants, animals or man, as the harmonious operation of the life force in an organism. This ideal harmony would include the sum of all energies and perfection in the development of structure. Harmony between all these would constitute health. Disease might then arise through failure of action, or overaction of any of these elements of force or structure. Regarding again the force side of the equation alone, as there is but one quality of life, viewed as an endowment of matter, so would there be but one kind of disease, viewed as a disturbance of vitality. While, then, life viewed as one in kind manifests or qualifies in an innumerable number of forms or concrete degrees, so disease, viewed as disturbed harmony or modified vitality, and one in kind, would be found to manifest a great variety of forms. The vitality, and the integrity of the structure in organisms, are definitely related to each other. These are mutually dependent. Not the slightest disturbance of either function or structure is possible without the other participating and suffering accordingly. In all matters of growth, repair, development and function, it is physiologically as correct to say that the function builds or exercises the organ as that the organ exercises the function. The relation and the dependence are mutual.

If these principles are true on the organic plane of life, in relation to structure and function, and no physiologist can successfully deny them, they will also be found to hold good on the higher plane where body and soul are concerned. The relation between body and mind will be found to be the same as between organism and function, or between structure and vitality. If in any sense the body can be said to build and to manifest mind, in the same sense can the mind be said to build and exercise the body. The dependence here, as in the former case, is mutual.

If the foregoing premise and reasoning be correct, then the prevailing methods of regarding health and disease are greatly at fault, for these pay great attention to vitality and structure, but almost wholly disregard the relation of body and mind. If the relation of vitality to structure on the one side is supplemented by the relation of mind to body on the other, what reason can there be for paying so much attention to vitality and so little attention to mind? We hear much about the necessary care of the body, and of its exercise to promote vitality, strength of life, and length of days; but we hear very little in regard to habits of thought, strength of will, and dissipation of energy in the mental realm. Imagination, the creator of forms and of all ideals, is left to run riot, or is indulged as a mere luxury, a beautiful or a depraved supernumerary of existence.

Every intelligent student of human nature is aware that any disturbance of bodily structure or function modifies mental function and power, and that whenever such disturbance is severe, or long continued, the mental alienation may also become severe. No so-called diseases are more common than hysteria and hypochondria; they often give color to a whole life, destroy all happiness, and render their possessors the most miserable of beings, besides entailing untold misery upon others. But slight physical disturbance in such cases can be discovered, certainly none that necessarily shortens physical life; nor is there great bodily pain, nor physical suffering, nor inability for almost any amount of sensuous indulgence or dissipation. There is often in such cases a wonderful ability to make everyone miserable. We are all familiar with persons who habitually indulge in fits of anger, jealousy, enviousness, greed, and all uncharitableness; and these persons seem to be unaware of the fact that they are molding their whole bodily structure to these vicious habits, so that in time it may refuse to express any other sentiment or emotion. The connection between body and mind seems to be wholly lost sight of. All evil passions and unworthy thoughts vitiate the bodily secretions, and in time mold the tissues so that the recurrence is automatic. It is by no means an uncommon occurrence for a nursing infant to be thrown into convulsions from nursing a mother that had recently indulged in a fit of anger, or to sicken from a mother's grief and unhappiness. These considerations and illustrations might be extended indefinitely to show the influence of the mind over the body, supplementing the influence of body on mind. Enough, however, has been said to show how basic are these relations, and that any concept of health, and any theory of disease must regard the relations of mind to body no less than of body to vitality.

Now, in the light of these considerations, what is health? We are not yet ready to answer this important question. In considering health in relation to vitality and structure, we have discovered that another factor enters into the account, namely, mind. If vitality be the motive power of the body, mind is its crowning glory; and just as the vitality may be weakened, vitiated or destroyed by vicious habits, so may the mind be deranged and demoralized by a similar process. Take from man all motive power, and all mental power, and his body becomes an inert mass, fit only as food for worms, or to be scattered to the elements from which it came. If health in its broadest sense is harmony, then that harmony concerns body and mind no less than body and vitality. What then is the normal relation of body and mind concerning which harmony is to be predicated and secured?

Mind is the immediate agent of the conscious ego on the one side, and on the other it stands as the concensus of all bodily faculties, sensations and feelings; or, in other words, as the translator of the outer physical world, through experience, into terms of self-consciousness. The body then, with all its functions and faculties, is the servant of the conscious ego, the real self. Mind and body therefore are equally servants of the real man. The sensuous life of man is directly related to the bodily structure and functions, and indirectly related to his mental life, while the results of all experience in these realms belong to the conscious ego, man's real individual life. The intellectual life of man is directly related to the conscious ego above, to the sensuous life below, and indirectly related to the physical structure. What we call mind is therefore intermediate between the ego and the body. Naturally the mind is the almoner of the real man, while the body is its servant to do its bidding—the vehicle of its will, and the servant of its commands. Here then is a community of interests with a centralization of power, but in the natural order this government is patriarchal. If the head directs the hands as to what they shall hold or not hold, and directs the feet whither they shall tend, by reason of the intelligence which the head possesses and which the hands and feet do not possess, the head preserves and protects both hands and feet as its own, as part of its very self, its trained and true servants and best friends. Each has need of the other. But suppose the hands and feet grow rebellious, and say to the head, we will no longer follow your bidding, we prefer our own counsels, and will go our own way; it is easy to see what will follow. The order and the design of nature are apparent. It would be no more absurd to allow the hands and feet to dictate the policy of government in the life of man than to allow his sensuous life, his appetites and passions, to rule rather than serve the real man. Harmony therefore means the rule of the lower faculties by the next higher in concrete degrees, and the supreme rule of the conscious *ego.* Everything short of this is the harmony of death. Peace secured on any other terms means final dissolution and destruction. In a well-ordered government, such as the nature of man is evidently designed to be, the *ego* sits a king upon his throne. The mental faculties are his ministers of state; the sensory faculties are his household servants, and never his masters. The vital powers are his standing army to protect his realm, and never to invade that of his neighbors, but able, in case of need, to relieve distress, protect the innocent, and promote the reign of peace and plenty throughout the world. When the king is thus enthroned, Health blooms like a rose on the outer walls of his palace, and harmony dwells within his gates. This is the meaning of a sound mind in a sound body; and the jewel that sparkles in the crown of the king is a spark of the Divine Intelligence, and it illuminates the whole palace as the diadem of divinity.

But alas! the king is dethroned and a tyrant sits in his stead. He dons the crown and boasts of its jewel, unmindful that its brightness is blackened as with fire. There is no tyrant like disease. His minions lurk in every drop of blood, and hold high carnival in joint and sinew; their bonfires glare in every organ, and set on fire even the mind, the palace of the king; they hoot at the tyrant, yet hasten to do his evil bidding. Crime is but another name for disease, and sickness and pain are but the disorder, bred by ignorance of the just laws of the rightful heir to the throne of life. It was not so designed; it ought not so to be. Whenever intelligent human beings shall take as much pains to keep their minds clean as to keep their bodies clean; whenever these shall realize that even perfect health, noble powers, and splendid opportunities are but the beginning of real life on earth, then only will man have entered his birthright, and begun to involve the divinity that is above him.

The progress of science is almost altogether in physical things, and the practice of medicine has little regard for anything beyond man's physical being. Insane asylums are crowded to repletion, and half the energies of those who are not actually disabled by disease in some form, or who are not classed and housed either as criminals or unfortunates, are demanded to take care of those who are thus disabled and sequestered. It is as though an army marching through an unknown land were kept busy caring for its wounded and burying its dead, when not in actual conflict with its camp-followers. Real progress is retarded if not impossible. The rule of nature is not the greatest good to the greatest number, but the greatest good to all; and she everywhere and at all times places over against the apparent progress of the classes, the real degradation, suffering and despair of the masses. If you think, my reader, that this is an altogether pessimistic view of things, I put but one inquiry: Is it not true? He who is clothed in the human form, and who therefore belongs to the great body, humanity; he whose lines have fallen in pleasant places and who is rich in basket and in store, yet who imagines that he has progressed away from the misfortunes and miseries of his kind, will find himself woefully mistaken. The miseries of humanity are indeed like a great stone, crushing out its life. He who will fall upon this stone with all his best endeavor shall break it; but upon whomsoever this stone shall fall it shall grind him to powder. Neither politics nor physic will cure the ills with which we are afflicted. More than half our diseases, counting criminals and so-called unfortunates, are of mental origin. Vicious habits of thought, greed for place, for power, and for gold, selfishness in every devil's garb, crush out the light of love and disease all humanity.

The laws of health are few and simple; the means of

restoration to health, where people are not hopelessly diseased, are usually simple also; but these laws and measures have strict regard to the mind as well as to the body, and no less to the body politic. We placard a house against smallpox, and disinfect against contagion, yet moral leprosy and mental distemper are seldom regarded as contagious. Everything possible is often done to increase the predisposition to disease in the young by encouraging precocity and disregarding malformation. If a child of tuberculous parents is born with a narrow chest and a large head, by the time he reaches the age of puberty these defects in the structural harmony of the body are often greatly increased, whereas they might be nearly, if not altogether eliminated by out-of-door exercise, proper diet, and mental repose. The statistics of consumption are a sufficient commentary. The doctors are expected to do with drugs what the parents might have accomplished by a little less worship of society, or mammon, and a little knowledge of physiology. The druggists and the venders of patent medicines manage to pick up a living, while the doctors waste a good deal of valuable time in collecting fees and gathering statistics for cases of tubercular disease! By the time these cases are brought to the doctors with cough, hectic, nightsweats, and emaciation, they are hopeless, and before this time warning is disregarded. The medical profession has been actively and faithfully engaged for many years in trying to discover the cause and prevention of disease, and the best service of the best physician consists in teaching people how not to be sick. Many persons in every community value the services of a physician according to the length of his countenance and the size of his doses. This offers a golden field to patent medicines, advertising quacks, and unprincipled scoundrels, and here as elsewhere the supply equals and sometimes exceeds the demand, and yet these people wonder that they are sick. The real province of medicine in the cure of disease is very narrow. The true application of physiology and hygiene in the prevention of disease and in the restoration to health is very broad. There is indeed in every community a large and increasing class of persons who are beginning to realize these facts, and though a single generation will not suffice to render them longer-lived, they have already greater confidence and greater comfort in life. The organization of schools for the training of nurses, and the better education of students in all respectable medical colleges, added to decrease of drugging and better regard for the laws of life and health in general, are hopeful signs for the future of humanity. As yet these are but feeble resources in the face of the ignorance, the superstition and the degradation of man. Fraud and imposture are always able to thrive on ignorance, and disease will disappear only in proportion as these recede.

The life of the globe is one in kind, so far as life is considered as a force inherent in matter. It may also be conceived that disease is also reducible to a single form as disturbed vitality. A mental emotion, indulgence of the imagination or mental friction is as competent to disturb vitality as any physical cause. In a great many cases of disease recovery is retarded or rendered impossible by mental conditions. Mental states are thus both the cause and the cure of many diseases, and mental conditions have a great deal to do in all diseases. It likewise follows that mental states ward off disease and promote health. It is quite evident from the signs of the times that these facts are being better understood, and that so-called mental cure is to have a far larger part to play in the future of medicine than has been assigned to it in the past. Intemperate, unreasonable, and untrue assertions, however, will not promote progress in this direction more than in any other. The mind is not all there is of man, nor is mind the sole cause of either life, health or disease. We have already indicated the relation of mind to body, and of the conscious *ego* to mind. There are bodily functions, like respiration, that are largely under the control of the will, and cases have been known where the exercise of the will could perceptibly modify the action of the heart. In ordinary life, however, there is no function of man less under the control of the will than the process of thought; and few individuals have any more power to prevent or control the surging billows of passion that sweep over the soul than they have to ward off malaria or small-pox from the physical body. There is no greater predisponent to disease than fear, which renders the body negative and disarms the mind of all resistance to all morbific agents. The characteristic phenomena of fear, influencing both mind and body, are more or less present in all disease, though these phenomena may arise from an innumerable number of causes. It is true that mental exaltation may render the individual unconscious of pain, and may even remove functional disease under certain circumstances. It is equally true that mental exaltation will result in insanity and cause death. Mere mental exaltation, therefore, is not necessarily a beneficent and curative process; nor will any mental state possible to man in his present condition of inherited disease and partial development be sufficient to remove his disability, and keep him well and happy for any great length of time. Such a result can only be attained through processes that fully recognize what man is, and what it is possible for him to become, and the philosophy which attains this result will not begin by ignoring the fact that man is a divine idea but partially realized—imperfect as to mechanism and function, and habituated by long practice and generations of inherited bias to disease, to sin and to death. This imperfect man is not in any broad sense a magician. A true magician is one who, from intimate knowledge of the laws and processes of nature, is able to bring about results that seem miraculous to those ignorant of nature's laws. It is true that enthusiasm and mental exaltation will sometimes accomplish wonders; but when these conditions are laid on a foundation of ignorance, and not on any real knowledge, the results are neither certain nor permanent. The assertions of ignorance are not always separated from the dicta of knowledge; the ignorant and superstitious know no difference between them.

Cheerfulness is a great promoter of health, and yet many persons are from temperament and inheritance morbid and melancholy. Antenatal conditions must be taken into account, and the load of depression accumulated generation after generation sometimes rests upon an individual with a crushing power that he is unable to withstand. The education of an individual is inseparable from his inheritance, and always commences long before he is born. Whenever parents begin to realize this fact they will be able to prevent many of those calamities that now entail untold misery.

What man most needs is a knowledge of his own nature, and of the laws of physiology that conduce to health of body, and health of mind. When man is in possession of this knowledge he will value it above rubies, and when, through the exercise of this knowledge, he has been able to remove all vicious habits, and to overcome inherited bias to disease and crime, then indeed, will the bright blood of health course through his veins.

Even in the face of all these acquired habits and inherited tendencies to disease restoration to the best degree of health possible under the circumstances depends far less on any drug action than on the correction of the vicious habit, be it of body or of mind. People often regard these measures as ridiculously simple, and in other cases are unwilling to forego the self-denial and take the trouble necessary to recovery. People often act as though they believe that, when sick, it is only necessary to consult a physician, pay him a fee, take a certain quantity of drugs, and straightway be as though the disease had never occurred. The vicious habit remaining unchecked, the disease of course returns, and so-called chronic disease is the result. Medicine no longer serves to arrest or modify the condition complained of, and the cure is now rendered often impossible. The result is a premature death or a miserable old age; but in the meantime the vicious habit is generally transmitted to posterity, and the final conflict, rendered constantly more difficult, is relegated to the coming generations.

These are the problems that are pressing for consideration. There is no end of new remedies, and new methods of compromise with disease; but there is far too little attention paid to the promotion and preservation of health, and toward this end the mental conditions, habits of thought, and ideals in life, have quite as much to do as any mere bodily function. We need less of mind-cure, and far more of mind-health; we need higher ideals in life, pursued with more zeal; we need a concentration of energies on more noble purposes; we need mental exaltation that shall be able to see beyond self, and that shall be supported by health of body, and thus be capable of unwearied exercise, and not unsettle the reason, nor relax into *ennui* and imbecility.

Reforms in medicine, like political reforms, come largely from outside demand originating with the people. With many noble exceptions, and in spite of the progress and liberality of the age, there is, nevertheless, more of bigotry, more of the spirit of intolerance and persecution in the so-called medical profession of today than among almost any other class of persons of equal intelligence. The reason for this may be found in the innate selfishness of human nature, so often placed on trial by self-interest. Those ignorant of the laws of life are in continual fear of death; ignorance and fear thus offer continual prizes to cupidity. Human nature is indeed everywhere the same, but selfishness does not everywhere have equal opportunity. The growth of selfishness, like that of any other vice, is often imperceptible; it is but another form of animal egotism, and it thrives best in an age of ignorance and superstition. Progress elsewhere in human affairs depends upon the diffusion of intelligence among the people, and progress in medicine offers no exception to the rule. Nothing will do so much to banish the fear of death as diffusion of a knowledge of the laws of life.

Unprofessional and even unprincipled persons have recently called attention to the influence of mind in promoting both health and disease. Many persons in every community have caught the new craze, and as a consequence there is a decrease in the sale of patent medicines and in indiscriminate drugging. If physicians would encourage a liberal spirit of investigation, and would rely less on denunciation, soon every honest student would be convinced that drugs are inferior to dynamics, and that the silent, and hitherto unrecognized forces of nature, are potent agents for both good and ill. Denunciation not only never promotes the cause of truth, but it often confirms people in error. There is, indeed, both room for improvement and need of progress at this point. Humanity will still offer a fruitful field for speculation, no less from a financial than from a philosophical point of view, and its only protection and elevation will still lie in the diffusion of knowledge among the masses. While ignorance remains, cupidity will flourish. Whenever among the people the real good is placed above the seeming profit; when health of body and health of mind are held as superior to sensuous enjoyment; whenever character is held as superior to conventionality, and whenever standards of right are valued above those of so-called society, then will the ideal become the real, and health will take the place of disease.

The condition called disease manifests its presence, first, through disturbed function, and even where tissue change is the first to be observed no such change has arisen without previous disturbance of function in the part involved. When, therefore, diseases are classed as functional and organic, the former precede the latter. The seeming exceptions to this rule where, for example, morbid growths arise, are classed as disturbances of the function of nutrition, and later on in progress of the disease, these morbid growths may disturb other functions in many ways. The length of time required for acute functional disease to become chronic organic disease varies very greatly. As a rule this change occurs very slowly, owing to the resistance offered by the vitality of the body. There are exceptional cases, however, where, from age or enfeebled constitution, the progress is very rapid. In the strictest sense there can be no disturbance of function without disturbance of structure, while every abnormal modification of structure changes the function of the organ or part involved. While, therefore, the most intelligent pathologist often experiences difficulty in determining in a given case whether important tissue changes have yet occurred, those ignorant of these basic principles of pathology often entirely overlook the difference between incurable organic disease and simple functional disturbance, and are as ready to promise a cure in the one case as in another. Just so surely as disease results in death, so surely is there a period during its progress previous to death when it is incurable. This point is never reached through impaired function alone. The old saying, "as long as there is life there is hope," is, therefore, often a fallacy. It is a singular circumstance that when an individual recovers from any given disease, the recovery is attributed to such appliances as have been made use of, no matter what they may have been, even though they may really have permanently impaired the health of the patient. Let any dozen similar cases of any disease be treated by as many different methods, some of them diametrically opposite, and with doses of drugs varying from the maximum to the minimum, and the practitioner in every case will claim credit for the cure, provided the patient does not die. If the patient dies, really from overdosing and malpractice, or from neglect of the proper remedies, or from any other cause, it is put down as an inscrutable dispensation of Divine Providence. We thus rob Providence of all credit for assistance

in case of cure, and load upon him all our misfortunes and
mistakes. There is no help for this condition of things except in better knowledge on the part of the people, and more
and better knowledge on the part of the practitioners of
medicine. The simple fact ought to be generally understood
that by far the larger part of simple functional disorders
tends to spontaneous recovery. It ought to be generally understood that such assistance as is generally required to restore a simple functional disturbance consists largely in hy-
gienic and dietetic measures, such as are dictated by intelligence. It ought to be generally understood, moreover, that
most of such cases will recover if they are not prevented
from so doing by pernicious interference; and finally it ought
to be understood that no person is properly educated who
cannot in some fair degree distinguish between functional
and organic disease. The pursuit of this knowledge should
be encouraged in preference to much of that which now
constitutes the course pursued in schools and colleges. The
first result of the more general diffusion of such knowledge
would be that the physician would be less frequently consulted. The second result would be the more frequent de-
tection and suppression of charlatanry, and the physician
would be consulted in serious cases before it is too late. The
result upon the medical profession would be that the genuine physician would be all the more appreciated. His occupation would indeed be skilled labor in the highest sense;
he would be to his patrons at once teacher, counsellor and
friend, and the upper ranks of the profession, open then as
now to all aspirants, would be measured by philanthropy no
less than by skill. Physicians have in recent times paid
great attention to the accurate diagnosis of disease. This
branch of professional work has indeed become a fine art.
It was formerly believed that skill in diagnosis could only
come by long experience. One year's hospital experience
to a young man well read in anatomy, physiology and diagnosis, is now really of more worth as genuine experience

than a dozen years of the happy-go-lucky experience of a generation ago. The more intelligent individuals in any community no longer require that their doctors shall be moldy like their cheese, as Dr. Holmes wittily puts it, well knowing that much of so-called experience serves only to deepen error and repeat mistakes.

From the foregoing considerations it is easy to determine what influence the mind may have on disease in general, and what class of diseases may disappear during mental exaltation, no matter how induced. These are strictly functional disorders. Unfortunately, very few indeed of the practitioners in the new craze called "mind-cure," "Christian Science," and the like, are any better able to diagnose disease than their patients, and they are as likely to promise or report a cure of cancer or tuberculosis in the last stage as in cases of hysteria or hypochondriasis. These people seem unmindful of the fact that dangerous cases may be criminally neglected, and that other cases will recover spontaneously if not interfered with. There is, moreover, another principle of equal importance relating to the function of the mind. If one were liable to fall overboard in mid-ocean, where nothing but swimming could save him, it would be the part of wisdom to try swimming. If one found himself overboard with no previous experience in swimming, he might intuitively catch the knack of swimming and pull out manfully till rescued; but the chances would be that in the excitement, bewildered by fright, he would drown. It has already been shown that the great majority of persons can no more control their thoughts, and concentrate their minds on a given idea, than by an effort of the will they can control the beating of their own hearts. If, then, no facility in controlling the mind and concentrating the thought has previously been acquired by an individual, and if he makes his first attempt at such control when under pressure of great excitement, or great danger, it is very doubtful if any appreciable result would follow, though a self-limiting disease, a mere functional disturbance, might coincidently disappear. Such disturbances are always more or less influenced by the will, and are sometimes purely imaginary. On the other hand, it is well known that will power may be cultivated, and by practice the mental faculties may be concentrated to the point of abstraction, or such concentration may even result in distraction. Such exercises are, to say the least, dangerous to those ignorant of the laws of mind; as optical disease and insanity have been known to result therefrom. An individual in whom the mental faculties have been wisely exercised and concentrated by the will may indeed fix his mind upon a given subject to the exclusion of all others; and according to the motives that actuate his life, and the ideals that inspire his soul, he may create blessing or ban, and promote health or disease. The exercise of mental concentration is one in which the poet, Tennyson, is said to delight, and he plainly refers to it in some of his most exquisite passages. For an individual who habitually neglects the plainest laws of health, and indulges many evil passions, to devote his time to mental concentration for the cure of diseases that far safer and simpler measures would prevent is, to say the least, an unmitigated folly.

It is not, therefore, difficult to predict the outcome of the mind-cure and the so-called Christian Science craze. It has its good and its evil side according as its cultivators are sincere and intelligent, or the reverse. It has already done some good, and a great deal of harm, and so will it no doubt continue to do to the end of the chapter, when some new craze will take its place.

To the intelligent student of human nature all such episodes present interesting psychological studies, and if he but examines them fairly and dispassionately they will prove valuable and instructive. If, however, he allows himself to become a zealous partisan on either side, he may follow, or fight the craze, and be no wiser in the one case than in the other.

The true student of human nature will be as passionless in the pursuit of truth as he will be earnest in applying and diffusing it for the benefit of his fellowmen. Reformers have, indeed, often been men of one idea, and unable to control the forces they have raised; new and often greater abuses have followed closely upon reform. The student of human nature must be a philosopher, and he may also be a philanthropist. He may not rouse a nation to anger, but he can inspire the souls of men with benevolence; and though he may escape fame, he will be certain of a peaceful life and a contented mind. In the present condition of society, when disease in some form is more nearly the rule than the exception, a large part of the resources and of the energy of mankind is necessarily employed to secure health. The records of premature deaths and incurable diseases show how inadequate, after all, are our efforts in this direction. It is indeed a rare thing to find an individual without an infirmity of some kind. We would soon become weary of listening to a musician who devoted the greater part of his time to the tuning of his instrument, and who could at best give us but snatches of harmony and mere glimpses of his power. The human mechanism is a most wondrous instrument, capable not only of producing simple harmony, but of repeating the symphony of creation. Health of body and mind, rare as that condition may be, is nevertheless the beginning, and not the end of existence. The struggle for mere existence, wherein man is obliged to wage perpetual warfare against the foes of health, can give little conception of the real ministry and destiny of man on earth. So long as this battle must wage man cannot be said really to have lived at all. In perfect health man is no longer at war with nature, nor with the elements of his own body. Health means perfect peace, and is the foundation upon which the harmony and the blessedness of life proceed. From this foundation the real divinity in man will go forth as an image of his Creator, and a co-worker with the divine. In the present condition of man this may indeed be an ideal life, but it is certainly foreshadowed by all lower forms of life, and heralded by all coming events as the earthly destiny of man —a condition that is neither incomprehensible nor unattainable. Among the devices of men there is to be found no royal road to learning, and no universal panacea for disease. In the divinely appointed ordinances of nature may be found both the royal road and the exemption from disease and suffering. These lie along the line of discernment and obedience to law—not merely the laws governing the body, or the mind alone, for even these do not constitute the entire man. If man obeys, as far as they are known, the laws governing the body, disregards the laws of the mind, and is entirely ignorant of the laws of the soul, or the higher self, he will still be at war with the very elements of his own nature, and he cannot possibly thus be in harmony with his environment, or essential being. Health transcends the mere physical conditions as man transcends mere matter and force, as harmony transcends all musical instruments. It is indeed true that, in its highest sense as complete harmony, health is an ideal condition; but nature never builds without ideals, and no superstructure that man has ever reared has amounted to anything except as it embodied and realized more or less completely these ideals of nature.* Man has discovered many things, but in reality invented nothing. The partial glimpses that man has gained of the laws and orderly processes of nature have but enabled him to devise feeble counterparts of her equally wonderful appliances for utilizing force, overcoming resistance, and transforming matter. He who builds without ideals, either in the outer world of sense or in the inner world of soul, is leading an aimless life, and is like a ship sailing a boundless ocean with-

---

*The architectural principles of Vitruvius have as a foundation the modulus of man, thus deriving nature's law of form and proportion from her most perfect handiwork.

out chart, compass, or destination, following the law of chances as to shipwreck, and after that as to death or rescue. Nor is man left in necessary ignorance of these ideals. So long as man deliberately chooses the seeming profit in place of the real good, and prefers a moment's pleasure and an age of pain to self-denial, which is but the struggle to rise, or as the stroke of the brave swimmer to reach the shore, just so long will man be sick in mind and sick in soul, and therefore sick in body. No desirable possession of the mind, body or soul is ever attained without a struggle. All earthly possessions cost us dear either to gain or to hold, and neither health of body, peace of mind, nor supremacy of soul are gained on easier terms, else would they be today the universal possession of man, in place of sickness, pain and death. One man plants a tree, well knowing that another shall gather the fruit. One man lays the foundation of a fortune that his progeny may wear the crown of wealth, and yet few labor to possess and transmit even physical health to posterity. The foundations of great fortunes are always laid in labor and self-denial, and so are those of health and holiness. Thousands of young people set sail in life really bankrupt in health and in morals. Vitality and fresh experiences in sensuous enjoyment may for a time tide over the impending crisis, but it comes at last, involving innocent souls in ruin; and so the calamities of life are transmitted and perpetuated generation after generation, and then the blame is referred to the sin of Adam, or the dispensations of Providence! Every bankrupt soul knows better, though the charity of friends may still conceal the lie.

The way to health lies through obedience to law, and the discernment of laws determining health lies in man's recognition of the fact that he is a complex being, a conscious spark of divinity embodied in matter, and that no part of his nature can be neglected or ignored without making the whole man sick. Mental, moral and spiritual diseases by far

outnumber those of the physical body, for in these are included every sin and every crime, and so long as man ignores these, and their relations to the physical, so long will
perfect health be an ideal of some other clime, instead of
the universal possession of humanity on earth.

Man is no more all mind than he is all body. The talk
now-a-days about "mortal mind," and man as being nothing
but God is meaningless. No man living, known to us today,
is all mind, all body, or all God, nor will man become all
God through pure imagination, more than by gazing at the
tip of his nose till he becomes cross-eyed. The perfection
of man lies in his working with and through his conditions
and environment toward ideal perfection, and that which
more than all else hinders his march to "the serener heights
where dwells repose," is this ignorance of his own nature,
and innate selfishness in relation to his fellowmen. Let him
work to remove these and the light of a new day will rise
in him, and the dawn of a new era will begin for all humanity.

> "I trust I have not wasted breath;
>   I think we are not wholly brain,
>   Magnetic mockeries.
>
> *   *   *   *   *   *
>
> "To shape and use. Arise and fly
>   The reeling Faun, the sensual feast;
>   Move upward, working out the beast,
> And let the ape and tiger die."

CHAPTER XIII.

SANITY AND INSANITY.

Health of body and health of mind are inseparably connected. A diseased mind in a healthy body, or a healthy mind in a diseased body, are alike incompatible. Health has reference to perfect harmony and complete development, and is therefore an ideal condition rather than a present reality. Progress along the line of normal development leads continually to broader vision and to a completer life. The goal of man is perfection; arriving at this goal, man will find himself in perfect harmony with nature and at one with divinity. Sickness and disease are therefore due to incomplete and imperfect development. The life of the animal is circumscribed by its own appetites, and limited by the necessities of its environment. The animal *ego* in man narrows his vision and limits his endeavors to the circle of self. Having transcended the animal plane the nature of man aspires to the next higher; and whenever he ignores or denies this aspiration, which is his human birthright, his whole nature tends to revert to the animal plane. Whole races have thus reverted to barbarism, and besotted individuals, even in communities of advanced civilization, are often thus bestialized. This condition often results when reason is first dethroned, and where the human qualities gradually fade out and give place to the animal instincts and appetites. Such human beings not only manifest the instincts of animals, but they are even more dangerous to society, for the lingering light of reason converted to cunning intelligence may with the semblance of beneficence clothe treachery in the garb of purity. When the object of the demon's treachery is accomplished or defeated, nothing can so chill the blood and terrify the soul as the shriek of his baffled rage or the howl of his fiendish triumph. The growl of the tiger or the roar of the lion are tame in comparison to the human voice thus degraded.

The numbers of the incurably insane in all civilized countries are counted by tens of thousands, and these cases are largely on the increase. Like the diseases of the physical body, mental alienation manifests every conceivable degree, and every variety of form, from the morbid and melancholy to the raving maniac. In recent cases, and in the milder forms of the disease, treatment is sometimes followed by satisfactory results; still, in spite of all advancement in the art of medicine, the number of incurable maniacs steadily increases. The number of the insane thus steadily encroaches upon the number of sane in every community, and this ratio of increase is likely to become still greater unless preventive measures are introduced, or remedial agents are instituted against this fearful tendency to insanity.

The intellectual advancement of the human race has been very marked even within the past few decades, so that within the memory of those now living the whole theater of the activity of man has changed. Culture in its highest sense cannot be confined to intellectual advancement; nor can real progress for man be expressed in the race for wealth, extravagance, and selfish indulgence. None of these things necessarily elevate man beyond the sphere where the animal *ego* reigns supreme. Man may be a highly intellectual or a highly sensuous animal, but he is animal still, so long as self rules, and so long as selfish greed, no matter how expressed, inspires his efforts and shapes his ends. In his exultation over the intellectual progress and material prosperity of the age man has forgotten his birthright and his immortal destiny. In "free and enlightened America" the struggle for life has been transferred from the physical to the mental realm. When the country was new and sparsely settled the percentage of those who were engaged in manual labor or physical pursuits was large, and literary pursuits and mental strain were the exception. The ruling passion in America today is to avoid manual labor, to secure wealth without toil, to indulge sensuous appetites, and in every way to promote selfish interests and aims. Mental strain has thus increased manifold, and bodily disease has given place to mental alienation and to the wreck of reason. The conservative and moderating influences of the old religions have been largely withdrawn, and in their place, to add to the mental strain and general confusion, have come that psychological babel, modern spiritualism, and that soul-destroying mildew, materialism. These innovations serve only to materialize all spiritual conceptions or tend to destroy all hope of better things, or kill out every noble aspiration of the soul. To add still further to the mental strain that the human mind must endure, so-called Christian science, rich in assertion and poor in lasting results, seems bent on crowding the mind, all unprepared as it is, into the subjective realm, the very highway to insanity. If any are disposed to regard this as a doleful picture let them refer to the statistics of insanity for the past decade, and if they will then but carefully consider the above bare outlines they will be forced to the conclusion that the half is not told.

The perfect development of an individual and the complete harmony that constitutes the ideal life, and which is the only complete health of the human being, may seem to many an impossible attainment, and thus give rise to discouragement. Every well-meaning and earnestly striving individual has only to remember that this ideal of health is none other than the ideal of religion, and that the effort to reach this ideal perfection is the effort to become Chrislike. That this goal may be reached in the present life by but very few is no reason for relinquishing all efforts toward its attainment, for no such struggle can ever be in vain, and if life continues here or elsewhere, under any conditions, it must bear with it the accumulated results of every earnest endeavor.

The best that can be said of any imperfect individual is that his face is set in the right direction, and that he is striving toward perfection. He whose cycle of life is bounded by self, and whose interests are all personal, no matter in what form or on what plane these interests may be expressed, is still tethered to the animal plane; he has not yet entered his inheritance nor claimed his birthright. The structure and laws of action of the human brain, and the laws of the human mind, all show that narrow views and selfish aims tend to unbalance and degrade the whole human being. The nature of man is complex in both structure and function, and a wide range of activities is therefore necessary to maintain its integrity. Nothing so dwarfs man as selfishness; nothing so broadens and elevates man as sympathy. If one engages in specific manual labor for any great length of time, the bodily mechanism conforms to the narrow range of activities and becomes deformed. If one follows a specific line of thought to the exclusion of all other mental exercise, the thoughts revolve in a circle that is continually narrowing, and the channels of which are constantly deepening till the entire process becomes automatic. Other organs atrophy for lack of use, and the entire structure thus becomes unbalanced. Many persons are thus possessed; only a few possess real knowledge. This condition of possession differs from monomania only in degree, and it is often thus only a question of time as to when real insanity will declare itself. There are four things that men most desire, namely, love, wealth, fame, and power. Greed for these narrows all individual life to the horizon of self, and the ravings of the insane might be classed as due to disappointment or even to success in one of these realms. Outside of the thousands of the actually insane there are other thousands who are thus drifting toward the same goal, or who are laying the foundations deep and strong for insanity in the coming generations of men and women. If one will but study the encroachments of greed for gold through all its phases down to the condition where in the midst of plenty the miser dies from utter want; if one will observe how slowly but surely every noble impulse gives place to the consuming passion, and how generosity shrivels as in a consuming fire, he cannot fail to be convinced that selfishness at last, in every form, overreaches self, and leads inevitably to defeat and ruin. Selfishness is indeed the father of every vice, and vice destroys its votaries like a very moloch.

The time has now fully come when our mental habits and intellectual states are of paramount importance. If the combined skill of the medical fraternity of the world is unable in any large degree to remove the results of mental vice and to restore the insane to intellectual health, it is time to inquire into the real cause of insanity, and to endeavor to find a method for its prevention. We continually measure what we call success in life by false standards. We are in urgent need of a sealer of weights and measures in the intellectual and spiritual realm, to protect our own highest interests from the worst of frauds perpetrated by ourselves. This standard is indeed not wanting, but it has been so misinterpreted and so misapplied that it has become of no avail. This standard is revealed in the Sermon on the Mount, and it may be summed up in one word, altruism. Rites and ceremonies, creeds and genuflections, the devices of man, have set at naught this divine measure of human conduct and human motive; these have indeed reversed the divine decree, and put the commandments of man in place of the commandments of God, and we are now paying the penalty for disobedience. Protests against this view of the cause of all our ills will come alike from the bigoted churchman, from the selfish ritualist, and from the scoffing materialist. The father of lies has not only usurped the throne of the Son of Man, but he has intrenched himself in the very house of the Lord, and he has taken the very bread of the children and cast it to the dogs. Zeal for proselytes and religious propaganda are often but organized egotism, selfishness and conceit, masquerading in the holy name of religion. No wonder that crime, disease and insanity run riot and threaten to decimate the human race. In the name of the sacred altars of religion corporations of selfish men gather tithes and amass millions, while the poor go unhoused and the little children cry for bread. To complete the sacrilege and emphasize the awful sarcasm in the name of Him with seamless garment and with no place to lay his weary head, this corporate selfishness expresses surprise and sorrow, and appoints seasons of fasting and prayer over the fact that the great hungry, surging masses of humanity turn away from the churches and scout with scorn the very name of religion! This may possibly, by misinterpretation in certain quarters, be called a tirade against religion and the churches; very well, my brother, call it what you will, but first inquire of your soul whether it is not true, and account to your conscience for the stewardship assumed in the name of the Christ. Nothing less than the truth will lift humanity out of the pit into which it has fallen, and restore man to health and sanity, and the truth must not only be told, but it must be lived by everyone who assumes the name of teacher, and who thus becomes his brother's keeper. If the sacerdotalism of the world would follow the example of a Tolstoi, and distribute its hoarded treasure among the poor, then would suffering and want be for a time at least unknown, and the sad face of humanity would reflect the divine radiance of Him who preached the gospel of benevolence to the poor. These hoarded millions lie between the great orphan, Humanity, and the cross of Christ. If there is selfishness in high places, what wonder that the ignorant masses worship the golden calf? Insanity and imbecility are fast devouring the royal blood of the old world so that the ravings of the maniac and the gibberish of idiocy are heard from palace to hovel, and insanity goes hand in hand with plague and pestilence.

The sanity of the human race is impossible in the face of physical degeneracy. Whatever anchors man to the animal plane tends to degenerate and bestialize. The one animal attribute that can thus degrade man is animal egotism or selfishness. The prevention of insanity therefore depends largely on the diffusion and exercise of the principle of unselfishness. The spiritual redemption of the human race is impossible in the face of disease of body and mind. The physical, intellectual and spiritual elements in the life of man are inseparable. There was never an individual who was spiritually pure and perfect, and who at the same time was mentally unsound and physically diseased, and there never will be such an individual. We send missionaries to the heathen while crime walks red-handed through our streets; we build hospitals for the sick and sanitariums for the insane, and mania and other mental diseases multiply in the land. Large masses of intelligent men and women vote religion a fraud, and life a failure, and declare that they do not know or do not care what comes after this life.

It is high time that every well-wisher of the human race should turn his attention to the nature of man and his mission on earth. The cause of our ills is not far to seek. All efforts to pry into the conditions of another state of existence have practically proved failures, and we may as well go to work in earnest to see what can be made out of the present life and its varied opportunities. Mental and nervous diseases will recede and insanity will lessen just in proportion to the broadening of our vision and the extension of our beneficence. Our idols must be dethroned and we must move to higher planes of life, and by breaking down the walls of selfishness we shall discover more exalted ideals, develop finer senses, enter on a new line of experiences, and begin to realize the life that is divine. Sanity will there be the handmaid of health, and disease and insanity will return to the swine to be choked by the receding wave of animalism which will then no longer degrade the human race or dethrone human reason. The children of men will be clothed and fed; they will be healthy and sane; and as the agent of divine Providence a regenerated humanity will then embody the Christ. We must pray with hands full of burdens, with hearts full of sympathy, and with feet bent on missions of charity. The leper and the insane will then be known at sight as he who is walled in by self, and whose little soul is unable to scale the walls which he has built by his own greed, and who is unable to draw the bolts and bars which he has forged in darkness while avoiding the light of charity and love. Health will then echo the harmony of nature, and sanity will reflect the Divine Intelligence.

CHAPTER XIV.

INVOLUTION AND EVOLUTION OF MAN.

In a work of this character where it is undertaken to handle familiar facts in an unfamiliar manner, where relations are traced that are often overlooked, and where coordinate results are pointed out not generally supposed to exist, a considerable number of repetitions are unavoidable. More especially is this the case in the present instance, where a single modulus is discerned as underlying the whole of nature, and therefore including man. It is necessary in the present case to refer frequently to this modulus, and to point out its varied forms of application. Thus the same principle will be stated in various forms which are reducible to the same result, for only in this way can the universality of the modulus be made apparent. The principles of involution and evolution have been frequently applied in the way of illustration, as also to illustrate special groups of facts. If these two principles are the inseparable poles of one law, and if that law is basic and universal, it might seem necessary to take a somewhat broader view of the law itself than is to be derived from any special application.

No intelligent student of nature at the present time, at all familiar with the large groups of facts in physics and biology constituting the theater in which evolution is thought to play so large a part, will be found ignoring or entirely denying the evolutionary theory. No intelligent biologist familiar with the ordinary facts of human physiology will for a moment deny that the outer unfolding of the body of man from germ to prime is an evolution, according to any fair interpretation of facts and an intelligent comprehension of the principle under consideration. Evolution as a fact is everywhere admitted; the ground of disagreement is in the application and interpretation of the law. In other words, the difficulty is not in regard to facts or laws, not in science or philosophy *per se*, but in the minds of men who variously consider and diversely interpret nature; and were it not for the fact that evolution has been supposed to explain the origin of man from lower forms of life, and so apparently to antagonize divine revelation, it is doubtful if anyone would think of questioning the law any more than that of gravitation.

The most pronounced opponents of the application of evolution to the origin of man seem to have misapprehended this application as suggested by the leading advocates of the theory of evolution. This misapprehension has been so often and even so recently pointed out by leading scientists, and moreover made so plain to every unbiased mind that it would here be out of place to go into details. It may be here noted, however, that opposition has been shown to the various attempts that have been made to show the evolution of religious belief, from the fact that with most persons individual belief is inseparable from original revelation, and this they regard as directly of divine origin. The idea that a divine revelation may unfold under natural law seems here to have been overlooked.

So far as we are now concerned with evolution, its application and interpretation only are involved. Evolution being everywhere admitted as a fact, it is applied to two separate groups of phenomena. In the growth and development of individual forms of life it is generally admitted with but slight qualification. In the progressive unfolding of species, and in the progressive advancement of man through lower organisms, it is frequently denied—not always denied as a factor, but as being sufficient to account for all results. The question then presents itself in this wise: Does that law or process which everywhere unfolds or elaborates individual organisms, flowing outward, and expanding from center to surface, also push the whole complex series of earth's organisms upward from lower to higher forms? To this inquiry one party answers unhesitatingly in the negative, the other answers in the affirmative with certain concomitants and qualifications.

Here again it would be out of place to go over the ground involved in the discussion, as many volumes have already been written on the subject by leading advocates of either side with the result of bringing the factions no nearer together than before, as each party in turn claims the victory over the other.

Looking now at the processes of nature and of life as a whole, no one on either side will deny evolution *in toto,* and no one will deny that it has greatly aided in the interpretation of natural processes. Looking again at the processes of nature and of life as a whole, there is another law discernible, operating equally and consistently with that of evolution, and capable, when equally well apprehended, of reconciling all the above-named discrepancies and disagreements. If evolution is indeed true, and is more or less a factor in all processes, as is generally admitted, any other law or process discovered, or hereafter to be discovered, must be capable of reconciliation with evolution, and must be shown to work in harmony with it, when the range and application of both laws are understood. This concept and basis of agreement is perfectly consistent with the sequence of all scientific discovery.

Because evolution has been the first to receive recognition, it by no means follows that it has forever pre-empted all the ground, particularly as it is not generally claimed for it that it explains all processes in nature. No one claims this much for evolution, therefore every sincere seeker for the real truth ought to welcome any suggestion from whatsoever quarter that promises a reconciliation of beliefs, and a further and more consistent apprehension of nature. All processes in nature, whether inorganic or organic, present themselves to the mind as an equation to be solved. In all physical problems, whether in applied mechanics or in nature at large, there is the problem of the parallelogram of forces, whereby the direction of force or momentum is determined, and whence equilibrium results. Without this law even the apparent stability of forms in the midst of unceasing change would be impossible. Thus contentions result in compromise, and discordant elements unite to produce harmony. There are the dual conditions of centrifugal and centripetal forces, of cohesion and disruption, of attraction and repulsion everywhere recognized. There is behind all of these the problem of mass or inertia over against all tendency producing movement of mass, or the inherent relation of matter and force. This duality runs through the whole phenomenal display of nature as the basic idea of our concept of atoms, and in the genesis and phenomena of all life.

Duality and manifestation are synonymous terms; either term suggests the other. All problems of life, as all problems in nature, present themselves, therefore, under this form of duality. No principle is more widely recognized than this, as in one form or another it is the basis of the higher mathematics which enter the realm of nature's highest display, and calculate not only the application of principles to mechanics, but determine the revolutions of suns and planets, and the changes of time and seasons.

The central idea in evolution is the natural sequence and co-ordinate relations of all processes in nature. The evolution hypothesis alone does not satisfactorily reveal these relations and determine this sequence. The unfolding of germs in the vegetable and the animal kingdoms is everywhere recognized as the process whereby individual organisms arise. Evolution here recognizes the duality above referred to, first, under the terms heredity and environment; and second, it recognizes the fact that the individual at any stage of development is an adjustment of these two sets of factors. The personality of man is, at any moment from germ to death, the result of all that he has inherited and all that he has acquired. Here, however, the process by which inheritance is derived is not the same process by which subsequent acquirement is brought about. In fact, these two processes are exactly the opposite of the other. That which is derived is drawn in; that which is evolved is drawn out. These two processes are to and from the center of life in germ or man. It is true that evolution recognizes the element of progress in the presence of the apparent persistence of forms, types, and species, and recognizes some element that tends to push forward all life to higher planes and toward more perfect ideals, and endeavors to account for improvement by the principle of natural selection and that of the survival of the fittest; and no doubt these principles are concerned in determining results. These principles, however, on the one hand prove too much, and on the other are inadequate to account for the ideal forms toward which nature everywhere and continually strives. In the case of man these principles of variation, without an underlying modulus, are quite sufficient to have long ago modified him out of existence. Natural selection and the principle of the survival of the fittest no doubt have a great deal to do in determining conformity to types, and may modify and improve pre-existing forms, but they could never have originated the ideals which are thus progressively unfolded.

In spite of the ebb and flow of life, the wax and wane of civilizations, the rise and fall of empires, there is some element that not only preserves the human type, but pushes it continually toward a higher ideal, and through all lower forms of life there is a prophesying of man; an overshadowing of the human form descends to the lowest types of organic life, as a still higher ideal overshadows man himself. The theory of natural selection and that of the survival of the fittest fail entirely to account for this overshadowing ideal. Even the worm at our feet is thus climbing the mount of transfiguration.

Nature reveals in all her processes one divine ideal, man. This ideal descends from man to the lowest form of life, and ascends from man to the perfect archetype. It has been shown elsewhere in these pages that the lower forms of life contain elements of man's nature both in form and function. It is as though the individual qualities of man were separately embodied in living forms. As we approach higher forms in the lower animals these qualities are grouped together. Every quality therefore may be conceived as existing separately, and every possible variation below man may be conceived as resulting from combination. As the series approaches man the likeness becomes more complete. Man thus epitomizes the organic life of the earth. The lower animals are fragmentary human beings; the higher animals are rudimentary human beings. Unless the sequence of nature stops with man, man is a rudimentary being of a still higher or more perfect form.

Viewing now all of Nature's handiwork within the range of human ken, all physical processes, from the busy play of atoms to the revolutions of suns and worlds, all organic processes from monera to man, the growth of a single germ, the modification of species, the progress of the human race, and bearing in mind the duality of all processes and the bi-unity of all manifestations, we find the operation of a two-fold law corresponding to the universal duality; this twofold law is Involution and Evolution.

In all physical processes moving outward from center to surface, in all organic processes, unfolding from germ to organism, the process is evolution. This is just one-half the process, one member of nature's equation. Every play of forces, every display of processes, from center to surface, is met and balanced point by point, in atom or sun, in germ or organism, in plant, animal, or man, by an opposite impulse from surface to center. The overshadowing ideal form thus reaches and is impressed upon the life-center, and furnishes thus the plan and specifications for the building that is evolved. Evolution is thus balanced by involution. This is the universal process in the solution of the cosmic equation.

The recognition of this dual law is the reconciliation of Science and Religion. If we call evolution materialistic, we may with equal propriety call involution spiritualistic, and neither term can be construed into a reproach. We know no more of the real essence of the one than of the other. We recognize the manifestation of matter and spirit as the two poles of being, spirit being involved and matter evolved; these two meet and blend in all created forms. The one gives power and ideal form, the other, structure.

From the dawn of life on the earth to the present moment, from the beginning of the unfolding of every germ to the complete development of the organism one Divine Idea overshadows and is progressively involved in every living thing. If evolution is seen in any instance as a *vis a tergo,* involution appears as a *vis a fronte.* In the apparent striving of nature all creation tends to the embodiment of the Divine Idea through the evolving of the living form, and these forms strive continually toward the modulus, man, impelled thereto by the in-dwelling, and overshadowing of the Divine Idea.

Nature is not then soulless or Godless. Involution is as rational and as thinkable as evolution. What Nature and Soul and God are, in their essence, we do not know. All that man knows is revealed through man himself. These things to us are our ideas of them, no more and no less. The thing in itself is in every case beyond us, and we know no more of the real essence of an atom than of the being of God. We can comprehend God only as we involve the divine idea and evolve the divine life. The center in us of these two groups of experiences is where God and Nature meet in self-consciousness. The expansion of this center is understanding; the illumination of this center is conscience; and the harmonious adjustment of God and Nature in us is at-one-ment. The divine likeness is at-one with the Divine.

The question then for us is not who builds, but how is cosmos built? Our idea of the Great Architect is no longer extra-cosmic, but intra-cosmic. In place of what Carlyle calls an "absentee God, doing nothing since the first Sabbath, but sitting on the outside of creation and seeing it go," we have the idea of the immanence of creative energy, creative power, and creative design in every blade of grass, no less than in animal and in man. Not an infinitesimal atom can escape this divine immanence any more than it can transcend the bounds of nature. If in our human idea God is infinite, then nature is boundless. God is at the center and Nature at the surface. These are the essence and the substance, the ideal and the real, unity in diversity, diversity in unity, and duality in bi-unity. These are Father-God, and Mother-Nature. "After His likeness created He him male and female. Male and female created He them." Man-Woman are then the two poles of the One Being. Man is concerned only with the present life and the present time. Self-consciousness is for man the ever-present now; now is his opportunity; now, the appointed time. Man has no more present concern with a world to come than with the worlds that are past. Past and future are related to man, the self-conscious *ego,* but they are not the *ego* itself. To ignore or despise our present opportunities, either from motives of worldliness or other-worldliness, is equally subversive of the highest and best interests of man. For man to ignore his present interests on the one hand, or to relegate them to another state of existence on the other, overshadowed by the fear of death and the terrors of superstition, is in either case to barter his birthright and to miss the full meaning of life. To ignore our highest present interests is to be time-serving. To relegate these interests to another sphere of being with the expectation of greater gain is to be self-serving, and these are but different forms of the same animal egotism. The religious ideals of the earth's benighted millions are ingrained selfishness, and these ideals reflected back in time and worked out in the lives of men have resulted in man's inhumanity to man, while the formulated motive of glory to God has disguised the ulterior object of glory to self. The difficulty lies not with true religion but in the selfishness of man, and man is as selfish in his religon as in all things else.

If all lower forms of life prophesy of man, so is man on each successive plane of being prophetic of a higher state. All natures strive in man, because he has reached the human plane into which the light of that which lies just beyond pours in a never-failing stream, while the light from the human plane illumines all below. Man thus focalizes the plane below and the plane above him, and all antagonisms thus resulting are but manifestations of the impulse already referred to, pushing man in common with all nature to higher and still higher planes. From the dregs of animal life man has derived the principle of animal egotism. From the plane next above him, man dimly discerns the divine principle of altruism. Man is thus but one-half human, and by the time he has become wholly human, or altogether humane, he will have become half divine; for so does one nature overlap the other, and he advances into the higher nature only as he shakes off the lower. Forever a pilgrim, man must drop the load of sin before he can pass the golden gates that lead to the delectable mountains; and he drops the load as he journeys on, while sorely pressed, and not during hours of ease and refreshment. When he is conscious that his load has vanished, lo! his enlightenment has already come. Life is thus its own elixir, and its office is transfiguration.

All over the world we hear the word *humanity.* Benevolent enterprises are everywhere set on foot, and humanitarian societies are everywhere organized. This humane impulse, even when misdirected, is still the dawning of the divine in man, the forgetting of self for others, the advancement of altruism over egotism. For science and civilization on the one hand, and for so-called religion on the other, to claim all the credit for this dawning of the higher life, is to confess embodied and organized egotism, nothing more. The impulse bringing about this result is older than all religions, deeper than all sciences, broader than all civlizations, higher than all heavens. It is the Divine Spirit animating and elevating all nature.

The humane impulse in individuals is the true sign of advancement from egotism to altruism, from the animal, through the human, toward the divine. This is indeed an education in the highest sense, but not in the ordinary sense as the term is apprehended. What we call culture may be as one-sided and selfish as any other acquirement of man. Here as elsewhere man may have an eye only to the main chance, to the best opportunity for himself in intellectual matters as in money matters. Strife and competition here as elsewhere often take unfair advantage and trample down the weak as unmercifully as in the halls of trade, or in the public mart. Whenever and wherever one must lose in order that another may gain, all profit becomes plunder, howsoever protected by law or glossed over by so-called usage and respectability. Popular education, mere intellectual acquirement, often ministers to pride and self-conceit, and therefore belongs to selfish egotism. Intellectual pride is no more altruistic than purse-pride. To the selfish and time-serving, altruism has no other meaning than the giving up of the present advantage, with the somewhat uncertain prospect of a greater advantage to be derived hereafter. The idea of rewards and punishments is inseparable from self. To forego self-indulgence here in order to secure greater self-indulgence and more exclusive privileges hereafter, for the poor and despised here to change places with the rich and honored there, leaves the sum of human misery the same, and no such philosophy has ever advanced mankind one step toward divine altruism. Hence it was shown a little way back that the devout and the time-serving may be on the same plane. We are not placed in this world merely to give it up for a better or a worse one, just as jockeys trade horses. Life may be likened to an orchard laden with fruit. We enter it hungry and famishing. Suppose that we pass from tree to tree and eating none, thinking that the next tree will produce more luscious fruit and repay us for waiting, till we have passed through the orchard, and the gates close behind us, the night comes on and we fall famished in the darkness, dying, and bewailing our folly and our wasted opportunities; surely we would be fools indeed. Suppose we again enter the orchard with the thought that any of the fruit is good enough as we see it bending every bough; suppose we see all around us children who cannot reach the branches where hang the choicest specimens; suppose we find there the weak, the sick, the crippled, and the blind who have not power to help themselves, and suppose we reach out our strong arms in every direction and gather all that we see, trampling down even the little children in our greed, and reaching the highest branches from the broken bodies of the sick and starving, and so gathering all the choicest fruit into our own garners, suppose we protect it by law, and set watch-dogs at every avenue of approach, and finally starve ourselves at last through fear of decreasing our store; surely again we would be fools indeed. This is the parable of the quails and the manna by which a stiff-necked and rebellious people were taught. In these two hypotheses the result is the same; selfishness defeats self and ends in failure here and everywhere; and selfishness is not altruism, even when transferred to the celestial kingdom.

"Mine and thine" is an inheritance from animal egotism. "The earth is the Lord's, and the fullness thereof," and there is enough in this fair earth for all humanity if the strong will only aid the weak. Altruism gathers that it may give, and delights more to give than to gather. Man is the almoner of the divine, and he who is permitted to give is far more blessed and more bound to give thanks than he who is compelled to receive charity. He who thus forgetteth self remembers God. Not a far off "absentee God," but the God immanent in all his works, whose Altar is the human soul, and whose Providence is the human hand.

If religion was the first to announce "Peace on earth and good will to man," superstition stood ready to obscure and make it of no effect. Wherever religion built her altars, superstition lit her fires of persecution equally in the holy name of Deity, and so the most atrocious cruelties have been perpetrated in the name of God. Even today the conditions are unchanged. Christendom builds magnificent churches to save souls, and magnificent iron-clads to destroy men. If the money devoted to these two purposes alone were distributed among the poor, hunger and want would disappear from the Christian world. If the rich and prosperous were really altruistic the poor and oppressed would not be anarchistic. The rich and the poor, therefore, are arrayed against each other because egotism is forever at war with altruism, because the animal is hostile to the divine in man.

It may thus be seen that in the higher problems that concern the well-being of man involution and evolution are equal factors, and that through this twofold law the entire nature of man is comprehended. Science working upward, and religion working downward, come to the same conclusions, and are therefore reconciled. The sequence of evolution and the sequence of involution meet in the conscious *ego,* revealing to man his own nature, and the principles upon which his progress toward divinity depends. Divine altruism is thus revealed, not as a mere matter of sentimentality, nor as speculative philosophy, but as the one principle in all its bearings that elevates man above the brute, and that enters the conscious life of man as the divinity that shapes his ends, inspires his life, and realizes his destiny.

CHAPTER XV.

The modulus of nature, or the pattern after which she everywhere builds and toward which she continually strives, is an Ideal or Archetypal Man.

This universal idea has been frequently referred to in the preceding pages as the key to many mysteries. Something yet remains to be said in regard to this ideal, for if it removes many obscurities in the work of nature, it also illumines the pages of revelation, and gives to religion a meaning commensurate with life and time; nay, more, it reaches beyond the veil that separates the world of matter from the world of spirit, and reveals the conditions of consciousness in a higher plane of being.

The evidence of the truth of such revelations lies in the co-ordinate relations of all human experience to consciousness. The futility of all discussion regarding the immortality of the soul that does not begin with some definite idea as to the nature and origin of the soul is everywhere apparent. If it be urged that divine revelation has already settled this question, it may be answered that, with those who accept such revelation as divine, and therefore authoritative, there comes endless confusion in the application and interpretation of revelation to individual belief and personal life. Over against the belief in immortality, and in supreme happiness awaiting a select few of the human race, is the belief that a large proportion of human beings designated as the wicked shall be destroyed or shall exist in eternal torment. Most religionists thus divide the human race; but most confusing of all is the estimate of the exact conditions that are to determine the above classification. The result has often been that one class of religionists assign to the dark side of the equation all other members of the human race, while the first class are considered as doomed by all the others. This condition of things is the legitimate outgrowth of the fact that modern belief undertakes to hold by ancient creeds, forgetting that both belief and creed are the work of man, and while they are claimed as derived from the sacred revelation, they are not a necessary part of it. It may thus be seen that the fault does not belong to religion nor to revelation *per se,* but that it belongs wholly to man. Until man has learned to distinguish between revelation and his own or other men's interpretations of revelation, he has not taken the first step in the way of understanding any religion, and least of all, his own.

The result of the confusion above noted has been to separate nominal Christians into three classes, namely, materialists, agnostics, and enthusiasts. The first class deny the so-called immortality of the soul. The second class say they do not know, and while they are inclined to doubt, they are, or intend to be, non-committal. The third class refuse to examine or discuss the question, but take it on faith, and feel the assurance within them; and these are by far the most happy and the most to be envied. Unfortunately all persons are not thus enthusiasts, nor can all of us silence the voice of reason, nor suppress the interrogations that continually arise. The enthusiast cuts all knots that theologians have devised, brushes aside all contradictions and mystifications, and at a single bound seizes hold of the goodness of God, determined to win heaven by simple faith and obedience. The number of nominal Christians far outnumbers these real Christians, who are consistent so far as enthusiasm can be consistent in anything.

In the face of all these conditions there has arisen of late years an unusual interest in all psychological studies, and few nominal Christians can deny that at one time or another they have consulted one having a familiar spirit, in the hope of getting a few grains of real knowledge with which to fortify their waning faith. What man or woman is there above the intelligence of the poor imbecile who does not desire a completely satisfactory answer to the question? If a man die, shall he live again, and how, and where? Many no doubt still take this matter on faith, but few are thus satisfied. Few, indeed, who have strong ties of affection, and who find the pathway of life broken by open graves, are thus easily reconciled.

The present writer would divert the discussion from the question of the immortality of the soul to that of the existence and nature of the soul that is to be lost or saved, that is to continue beyond the grave, or to cease at the death of the body. If the lines of study herein suggested shall remove a great deal of obscurity, and so lead up to the other question with clearer apprehension of the nature of the problem, something will be gained. The terms soul and spirit have been so long used indiscriminately, and have been used to express the most diverse and fantastic ideas of innumerable persons, that it would be found exceedingly difficult now to attach any definite meaning to them. This is rendered still more difficult from the fact that very many persons now-a-days deny the existence of either a soul or a spirit in man, regarding all of man's powers as an affection of matter due to organization. But no one will deny the fact of his own consciousness. No one can fail to recognize certain conditions of consciousness in relation to thought, feeling, emotion, desire, and will. No one will claim to have exhausted the whole range of human experience, or to have completely comprehended any subject. Everyone can see that while the avenues of sense are many, consciousness is the one center toward which all sensations proceed. If consciousness be thus seen to be the central fact of man's being, and that through which all planes and conditions of life are related, then if man has a soul, or a spirit, consciousness must be the central fact of the soul, as of the bodily life of man. If the physical body is thus viewed as the vehicle of consciousness on the objective plane, the soul may be considered as the vehicle of consciousness on the subjective or spiritual plane. If man's experience here and now can be shown to be derived from both the natural and the spiritual planes, then the soul is within the body, and consciousness within the soul. If consciousness is within the soul, and the soul is within the body, then the body is the theater in which to study both soul and consciousness. If man's experience is his sole method of knowing and becoming, and if his experience now is derived from both the natural and the spiritual worlds, and if consciousness in man is thus open or may become open to the spiritual or subjective world, then the present life and the human body present the opportunity for study of man's life and experience in the spiritual world. If all experience of the natural world reaches consciousness through the bodily avenues of sense, and if the body and its avenues were destroyed or removed, leaving the soul, so to speak, naked, then any experience reaching consciousness thereafter would pass through the soul only, and so reach consciousness independent of physical avenues of sense. It has been shown herein that the body of man is conscious as a whole, and that of this diffused consciousness, self-consciousness is the center. At death both consciousness and self-consciousness leave the body. The soul then, the organ of self-consciousness, in passing to the subjective plane changes the basis of experience, and receives impressions direct, instead of through channels of sense. If consciousness now, while in the body, receives impressions from the subjective plane independent of the avenues of sense, there is nothing to hinder it from continuing to receive such impressions, and in larger measure after the body is thrown off. Consciousness may be seen to be related to time and sense, and yet not dependent upon these for its existence.

It may thus be seen that a knowledge of the planes and conditions of consciousness in man, here and now, is the only way by which man can really know anything of a future life, and that this knowledge of the planes and conditions of consciousness can only be gained by experience. In this way only can the gap between the present and any future life be bridged. We must experience the divine life in order to know that it exists, just as we must experience the natural life in order to know that it exists, and in either case the range of our experience is the measure of our knowledge.

Man's real knowledge is thus limited by his experience, and as this in any or all directions is necessarily limited, man knows nothing as it is, but only as revealed through his own partial experience; that is to say, he has his own partial and limited ideas of things. Man has thus an idea of God, of nature, and of himself. Man has only the least idea of that with which he is most familiar, namely, himself. If man could but know himself he would speedily change his idea of both God and nature. The reason why man knows so little of himself is because his vision is circumscribed by the narrow bounds of his own selfishness. He is thus anchored blindly to that animal egotism whence he came, and discerns not that divine altruism toward which he tends. Man thus narrows the range of his experience, and precludes the possibility of knowledge, and he will make nature's ideals conform to his own narrow ideas.

It is thus that man has an idea of God, and this idea takes on two forms, or is derived from two groups of experiences. Man views external nature, the phenomenal world of matter, force, motion and shapes existing in space and time. He sees the mighty sun and all the heavenly orbs rolling in space, the green earth putting forth blossom and fruit, and again cold and barren in winter. He sees the huge leviathan sporting in ocean deeps, and again the organism whose theater of life is a drop of water, and through all these he discovers system and order. The seasons come and go; nature blossoms and decays. Reflecting in all of these, the rolling thunder, the flashing lightning, the movements of life, the order through all, and the power over all—an unseen power behind a visible nature—man derives thence an idea of God, and this idea thus derived is pure pantheism.

Man derives his idea of God through another source. Looking inward into his own soul and taking cognizance of his own mysterious nature filled with hopes and fears, with joy and sorrow, aspiring, despairing, ferocious in hate, yet gentle in love, he thus realizes his own personality. Man thus finds power without and power within, mystery without and mystery within, and he thus adds to his pantheistic idea derived from external nature the anthropomorphic idea derived from himself, and he calls this idea a Personal God. Now let us suppose that this idea of personality were derived from a perfect man, then the ideal man would be the Personality of God. We should then have a nature-God and a man-God derived from the conception of a perfect personality. This idea would be strengthened and elevated, if one who had attained this human perfection were known to us, or clearly represented to us. Such an one would be henceforth our ideal man, God revealed to us through human perfection. If now the manner of life of such an one were revealed to us, and the means by which he had achieved perfection, then the possibility of our attaining to such perfection would be beyond all things inspiring. No personal God can be revealed to us except through man.

Nature to us seems wrathful and all-devouring, and the natural man outdoes even nature in cruelty and destruction. The Divine man is full of all sweet charities, tender, merciful, loving and approachable. He calls himself brother; he enters the lowest estate that the poor and despised may claim fellowship with him, and sickness, sorrow and sin disappear at his approach. If these attributes reveal the personality of God, as a divine altruism, a tender sympathy for all human woe, and a strong helpfulness for all human weakness, then this ideal reflected back on man's idea reveals the higher-self in man, and it reveals the means by which the higher-self may be realized.

We are here dealing with man's idea of God. Here profane history is to be entirely ignored as having no bearing on the externals of either the Christ or scripture. Neither has any discussion of the conception or birth of the man Jesus anything to do with the matter. The immaculate conception of a human being is something that cannot be understood and need not be discussed. The mystery of Christ must be sought in another direction if it is ever to be unveiled to the human understanding. The mystery of Christ to man is the mystery of the perfect to the imperfect. It is the mystery of the realized Divine Ideal to the imperfect human idea.

Christ is called "the only begotten Son of the Father." Let us suppose that from the bosom of nature in the fullness of time there was to emerge a perfect, ideal man, that the Infinite Power behind all phenomena had from the beginning this archetypal man in view, and that the purpose of all life was to realize this ideal, not once for all, but everywhere as the ultimate of all forms. The ideal man, Christ, was thus with God from the foundation of the world. Christ being thus the Divine Idea realized, man is a divine idea unrealized, or in process of being realized. The only begotten of the Father are thus perfect men, and the perfect man is embodied altruism. This method of viewing *Christos* may seem to the reader heterodox; but if he will bear in mind that the only way by which mankind has been able to reconcile the God-idea and the Christ-idea is by the interposition of an incomprehensible mystery, he may find that the mystery here interposed between these two ideas is not beyond comprehension, namely, the mystery of the perfect ideal man to the imperfect man. Without changing the facts this view brings God, and Christ, and man nearer together. The inconsiderate will moreover object that this idea makes Christ out to be only a man. But it cannot be said that a perfect man is only a man. We have already shown that one plane of life overshadows another, and that the perfect man involves the divine and thus realizes the divine ideal. It is thus the God in man that perfects him.

Let us briefly consider what view this idea suggests of the nature and mission of man as we find him in the world today. The perfect man, so far as he is related to time and phenomenal existence, is of slow growth. He is a man of sorrows, and acquainted with grief; he is to be tried and tempted at all points, so that knowing all evil he may consciously and deliberately prefer all good; he is through experience thus to become a conscious center of goodness, wisdom and power. Thus accomplishing the divine will and becoming the divine ideal, man arrives at perfection. In another section it has been shown that by the time man becomes altogether human, or humane, through altruism, he has become half-divine, having eliminated the animal egotism. The further unfolding of the divinely human man, by which he arrives at perfection, concerns the unfolding of consciousness on the subjective or spiritual plane of being, and the assumption of those powers that Christ predicated for them that believe.

The perfect man is a co-worker with God. His members no longer war with each other, and he is thus at-one with God. The attainment of perfection is thus the reconciliation of the human to the divine. If this ideal perfection has been even once realized, and if the experiences of life be regarded as a journey toward it, the brotherhood of Christ to man has a real meaning. But if Christ is God in some other, far-away and unapproachable sense, then Christ can be little to us.

The scriptures reveal an ideal man as one who had attained to all perfection, in whom dwelt all the fullness of the God-head embodied. The man-Jesus was crucified; the God-Christ was glorified, and so it is everywhere, and at all times; the crucifixion of the human is the enthronement of the divine.

The whole aim and meaning of human life thus becomes a continual striving after ideal manhood and ideal womanhood. Just as all lower life climbs toward humanity, so humanity climbs toward divinity. In the scriptures Christ is the embodiment of altruism, as Satan is the embodiment of egoism. Each is an ideal, the one placed over against the other that man may not err in his choice of methods or of ends. Christ is lifted up and draws all mankind unto Him through the sympathy and love of his divine benevolence. Satan is cast down, and drags man after him through their participation in his supreme selfishness. These are ideals of the lower and the higher self in man; and these two strive in man for the possession of his will, his consciousness, and his life. The selfish *ego* belongs, as we have elsewhere shown, to the receding wave of animal life. Man leaves this behind him as he journeys toward perfection. The conscious individuality belongs to the advancing wave involved from the divine life, and this unfolds and is illumined as man journeys toward perfection. Nothing can be plainer than this as the real meaning of human life. It is a great mistake to suppose that birth is the beginning and death the end of man. An endless future necessarily implies a measureless past. What we call time is a span between two eternities, the whence and the whither; and when time drops out, eternity only remains. It would be as correct to say that we die into this world and are born out of it, as to say that we are born into it and die out of it. Our mistake of the meaning of life includes a mistaken idea regarding both birth and death, and we have previously shown the evidence of this mistake in the fact that we have allowed fear and foreboding of evil to gather around the exit, which is painless and beneficent as a baby's sleep, and have come with rejoicings to welcome the entrance, which is often an *inferno* to both mother and child. It is thus that man's ignorant and superstitious ideas have reversed the beneficent will of nature, and reduced divine ideals to grotesque and horrible caricatures. No wonder that the despairing soul cries:

> "Alone! alone!
> Forth out of the darkness,
> Back into the darkness
> We come and we go alone."

Whence then comes the light to the despairing soul alone in darkness? It comes from within as a revelation of that divinity which lies at the very foundation of the self-conscious life of man. Divine-consciousness in man is illumination. This is the mystery of self-consciousness, and it can be no more comprehended in terms of sense and matter than the senseless rock can comprehend the sympathies of man. Naught but a spark of the divine would be capable of unfolding even to man's present estate, so that by experience he could epitomize all lower life; and naught but the divinity in man could lead him even through hope and desire to still grander possibilities of being.

The fact of a double consciousness in man is demonstrated by somnambulism. Man continually leads a double life. The subjective plane of experience is as patent and demonstrable as the objective, and the fact that man fails to distinguish between these two planes of consciousness, and is unable as a rule to assign his varied experiences to the proper plane, proves nothing to the contrary. This will be still more apparent when we consider that, as consciousness is the one center into which flow both lines of experience, and that all experiences of one plane are necessarily mixed with those of the other, it therefore requires a wider range of experience on both planes, and a high degree of consciousness to preserve the difference and trace the analogies.

There are thousands of individuals today who are conscious of experience more or less clear on the subjective plane of being. Many of these can enter this condition at will. In other cases it may be readily induced by artificial means, such as magnetism, and the use of drugs. Most of these artificial methods of inducing subjective consciousness are attended with great danger to the subject, and with very grave responsibility to the operator, who in depriving an individual of his self-control and impressing upon such persons his own personality, whether good or bad, must in some measure at least become responsible for the future acts of his subject.

In that profound psychological study, Bulwer's *Strange Story,* when Margrave came under the influence of the magic wand, now in the hands of his victim, he was not only helpless, but he was compelled to tell the truth. This is a universal fact in magnetism. The magnetic subject may be a villain in his objective state, but as soon as his objective life becomes obscured and the motives of egotism are laid at rest, he comes under the dominion of his higher self, and confession of crime and self-condemnation are often the result. The voice of conscience is no longer silenced by the senses and by self-interest, for consciousness on the subjective plane discerns only the real interest. The individual while conscious on the subjective plane may acknowledge and deplore the evils of his daily life, and yet predict that he will return to and continue in them, for he recognizes the conditions that have woven these chains of sense and self about him, and he knows that his will is unequal to the task of overcoming them. He must work out the evil *Karma* that he has engendered.

It is such facts as these that reveal the existence of the higher self and its relations to the two planes of consciousness. If now the life of the individual on the lower physical plane be inspired by the principle of altruism which leads him into all good and to do good, the nature of the individual is no longer at war with itself. The lower and the higher self are thus at-one, and the consciousness of man draws experience from the two worlds. Intuition, which is the direct apprehension of truth, unconditioned by sense and time, and which is the organ of the higher self, now supplements intellection, which is the organ of the lower self, through the function of the human brain. This union of man's higher and lower nature is called *the true illumination,* and it has been often achieved in all ages—not by the rich, the powerful, and the great, as men estimate greatness, but by the lowly, and the humane, by the despised, the poor, and the crucified, by those who having become dead to the world except as partakers in its misery, were alive to God; their *Adonai* had come.

If the reader shall say, this is all very beautiful, but it is transcendental; it may do for a romance, or a strange story, I ask him then what he can make out of the mystery of life or the fear of death? I ask him to reconcile nihilism, agnosticism and spiritualism, and give the true meaning of magnetism, hypnotism, clair-audience, clairvoyance, and the consulting of familiar spirits, a meaning and a use that is not transcendental. Is man then hopelessly bewildered and irretrievably lost?

I hold that true religion and true science come to the same conclusions. I hold that man's most bounden duty and his highest hopes demand that he shall know himself—not the selfish-self alone, that recedes and finally disappears as he journeys toward perfection, but also that higher-self that expands, illumines and inspires the ideal life. I hold that this higher self, this divine ideal is the modulus of nature, and therefore the true meaning of life. The Christ-idea did not originate eighteen hundred years ago. *Christos* was in the bosom of the Father *from the beginning.* Man has forgotten the civilizations that are past, but mother earth remembers all her children. These buried civilizations have tramped like mighty armies all round and round the globe.

Every hillside is a necropolis, and every valley is filled with dry bones. The dust of ages covers the remains and crumbles the monuments of man. Submerged continents bear down to ocean beds the cities of dim ages past. Where was the Divine Father during all these eons of time? Think you my brother He was sitting on the outside of creation, and only waking a few years ago to the nature and necessities of man? Alas! our ingrained selfishness is not satisfied with degrading man, it must also belittle God. Is Nature's modulus revealed today in every breathing thing, a lucky thought of the All-Father for the benefit of his peculiar people but yesterday, while in the earth's more ancient prime things came and went by chance? Is our salvation less today because those of old were also in the hollow of His hand? Divine altruism cried: "Come unto me all ye who labor and are heavy laden," and the buried ages heard, and it echoes to the ages yet to be. All nature climbs toward God as suns and worlds unfold.

> "Yet I doubt not through the ages,
> One increasing purpose runs,
> And the thoughts of men are widened
> With the process of the suns."

With shaded eyes and bended head man dimly discerns the mystery of life. In every clime God's altars rise; in every land and every age man feels the touch of wings, and dimly sees as through a veil his overshadowing Lord. What matters it the name he bears? Who knows the one true name? The highest name in every time has been man's highest ideal, and this has not been derived from selfish beast, but dimly seen as an overshadowing presence to which man gave his highest thought, his choicest gift. This ideal does not change, though it seems to recede as man advances, and apprehends more of the divine beneficence. To the highest soul it is most revealed, as distant landscapes blossom forth on nearer view from mountain heights. Man has foolishly imagined that he could hedge divinity about and appropriate it all to himself, and thus *our* God has been invoiced with our other possessions. 'Tis then we know the least of God, when we make of him a chattel.

Symbolize truth as we may, the greater mystery is the journey of life, and the great revealer is man's higher self, the overshadowing presence that draws him up toward diviner things. He who listens to the voice within his own soul will learn his own nature; it will be revealed from within. Self-consciousness illuminated will become divine consciousness, and the more the divine is thus revealed the more will man find himself powerless to define it. It will still be his highest ideal, and every higher plane revealed will show still higher planes beyond. The rude savage who worships a fetich never doubts his power to name or even to make and to mar his god. The illuminated soul with introverted vision is silent, for he finds neither name nor quality befitting the All-Good, man's idea of God. The higher self, when fully revealed and set free from the bondage of sense, will be at-one with that Elder Brother, the Christ, a living presence in every illumined soul, a co-worker with the divine for the uplifting of humanity.

*   *   *   *   *   *   *   *

In these pages no system of philosophy has been attempted, but a systematic use of the knowledge of common things has been suggested. Nature everywhere reveals system and order, but no system of philosophy promulgated by man has ever compassed the order of nature, or embodied the whole truth. The so-called originators of the world's philosophies, and their enthusiastic followers, have often imagined that they have arrived at finalities, when in fact they have but dimly discerned at best a few great principles. In the application of a principle to the processes of nature man always works from incomplete, and, therefore, insufficient data. The conditions of a complete system of philosophy, such as should stand through all time, would demand a complete knowledge of nature and of man. On the other hand, the inductive philosophy alone is insufficient. If, however, while pursuing the inductive method of research, as heretofore shown, proceeding from fact to law, we make tentative deductions, holding them strictly as such, and viewing them often in the light of experience, we shall thus hit upon a method of study and observation of incalculable value. We may not, indeed, arrive at final truths, but we may feel the assurance that we are on the way that leads to them. If man will but apply the principles everywhere revealed as the foundation of human nature, to the unfolding of his higher life, he may accomplish in the journey of the soul what modern science has done in the march of mechanics.

The dawn of a new era in the life of man is heralded by many signs. The apathy that arose from discouragement has given place to the humane impulses that have arisen from even a dim discernment of the needs and the possibilities of the hour. The leaven of benevolence is at work, and sweet charity and tender piety go forth as on wings of angels to relieve distress and comfort the despairing. Womanhood, the new messenger of divinity, is thus trying her long-pinioned wings and uplifting the human race through the immeasurable forces of gentleness and love. The soul of womanhood will no longer be chained to a crucifix and hedged about by the creeds of men. She will arise in the beauty of holiness like a true daughter of Zion, and open the Gates of Peace that all who will may come in. Look at her deeds of charity and her missions of mercy, and read in them the signs of the times. She has not even yet fully entered her kingdom, but she already has lifted humanity nearer to divinity than have the iron creeds of man for ages. The power is hers, but she must banish the last vestige of scorn for those of her own sex who have unfortunately become the victims of man's betrayal; she must realize that sin and crime are but the resultants of diseases that are born

of ignorance and innocence, and brought about by the selfishness of both man and woman; and she must also appreciate the fact that none need the ministry of love and kindness more than these sin-sick souls. Woman must be true
to her womanhood before she can inspire man to virtue. In
no age has the degradation of woman been contemporaneous
with the true elevation of man. The fortunate, the upright, the untempted—these are not the needy. Only they
who are sick are in need of a Physician such as Christ ever
was, such as woman is designed to be. Let it be understood
that every helpless, ignorant, orphaned daughter is the *pro-
tege* of every pure and noble woman in the land, let her ruin
be regarded as a universal disgrace to her sex, and let justice be meted out to her betrayer, and there would be thrown
around the possible victims of man's innate selfishness a wall
of protection that no man would dare to scale or break down.
The adoption of such a code of moral ethics would elevate
man and woman alike; woman would be saved from man,
and man saved from himself.

> Selfishness is the father of vice;
> Altruism, the mother of virtue.

There was a time in the history of man when he might
have been regarded as a healthy being. With the progress of
so-called civilization, and of the intellectual development of
the race, nervous maladies have largely increased. The
battlefield of disease has moved higher with the unfolding
of man's higher perceptions, and both mental and moral diseases are now more often seen than mere physical maladies.
Mankind begins dimly to discern this fact, though its methods and medicines may be likened to those of the middle ages
in the treatment of physical ailments. The Way to Health
now lies through co-ordinate harmony of man's entire nature. He is a laggard in learning and a blind student of human nature who believes that any system of drugging or
any method of mental exaltation now known is sufficient for

the promotion and preservation of health. Health must flow down into man's physical life from the harmony of his intellectual and spiritual nature. Health must flow up into man's spiritual life from the harmony of his natural and physical existence.

It is said that, when the first rays of the rising sun beamed on the statue of Memnon, it emitted in the midst of its brazen splendor the confluence of harmonious sounds. Even so the physical life of man awaits through the long, dark ages of superstition the rising glory of a brighter sun whose rays shall illumine his entire nature, till it responds without discord to the symphonies of creation.

CHAPTER XVI.

THE OUTPOSTS OF SCIENCE.

The diversity of intellectual pursuits and the multiplicity of scientific investigations and discoveries at the present time are indeed bewildering.

It is practically impossible for any one mind to compass or contain it all, or even to fairly epitomize it. There are, however, certain outposts in the general trend of thought, and critical experiment along scientific lines, that may be clearly discerned, and, at least, approximately formulated.

These outposts not only clearly indicate the trend of the times and the lines of progress, but at the same time they serve to indicate the quality of thought and the measure of intellectual evolution at the present time.

We are on the eve of some of the greatest discoveries known to man. Great as is the activity already referred to, it is quite equalled by a feeling of uncertainty as to many things hitherto held with great confidence; and over all there is an air of expectancy. No one knows, and no wise man would undertake to say, what might or might not happen in the next year, or the next decade.

The inductive method of Aristotle, since the time of Sir Francis Bacon, has given the impulse to modern science, and is largely responsible for the activity and the results already referred to.

In the foregoing pages of the Study of Man crass materialism, under the garb of science, has been often referred to. This materialism was a tentative, and perhaps a necessary result, of the method of investigation pursued, and of the subjects under special consideration.

Concerning Cosmology, and the evolution of the human race as a whole, little was generally known previous to the writings of Charles Darwin. The account in Genesis was neither altogether admitted nor denied; though often and diversely "explained," it was nowhere understood. Then came Darwinism, and "the struggle for existence in the midst of a hostile environment." The perpetuation of the species was the great burden of Nature and became the slogan of the evolutionist.

The individual was apparently for the time being ignored. There was indeed a forecast, that the race—some future race of human beings—would arrive at perfection, but as such fruition was likely to occur some millions of years hence, our solicitude for posterity gave little present comfort and less hope to the individual. In the meantime Nature was represented as quite regardless of the individual, and as continually sacrificing them in myriads to preserve the species. If the scientist of these earlier days were asked about the destiny of the individual, or the probable existence of the human soul, it was his "busy day," and he was likely to reply that *science* had nothing to do with such a subject!

In the meantime other scientists were steadily pushing their investigations in the realm of physics and chemistry into the constitution of matter, and the whole realm of dynamics, kinetics, and the like.

Spectrum analysis had afforded many interesting facts and broad philosophical conclusions. The wave theory of light and all previous concepts of the constitution of the *atom* were found erroneous by actual experiment, or entirely inadequate to explain facts and phenomeny often demonstrated.

Interest focalized in the *Ether*. Postulated as a necessity to account for the phenomena of light, it was now realized that in it was to be sought the origin of both the substance and the energy designated as matter and force on the physical plane.

Lord Kelvin is said to have proved by a series of careful experiments that all matter in the universe is, at bottom, ether.

This ether is indistinguishable from space. It is not ether in space, but ether as space.

The vortex-ring theory of Helmholtz gained credence rapidly, and thus a new theory of the *atom* came to the front.

"If a ring could be produced in material not subject to friction none of the motion could be dissipated, and we should have a permanent structure possessing several properties, such as definite dimension, volume, elasticity, attraction, and so on, all due to the shape and the motion involved. Imagine, then, that vortex rings were in some way formed in the ether, constituted of ether. If the ether be, as is generally believed, frictionless, then such a thing would persist indefinitely."*

If the grossest forms of matter are resolvable into ether, and the primordial atom consists of a mere *whirl* in this frictionless, imponderable, and continuous ether, exit materialism! and enter spiritism!

"Matter is a mode of motion of spirit," says Calthrope.

Now let us for a moment return to the evolutionists, and the followers of Darwin. Professor Huxley had been the prince of agnostics, and by inference he had often been classed with materialists. The "Unknowable" was an intellectual dust-bin for troublesome or impertinent questions.

NOTE.—It is interesting to read in this connection the theory of Descartes regarding vortices, and that of Leibinz regarding monads and atoms. The emphasis laid upon the principle of pre-established harmony, and its manifestation through mathematical laws on the one hand, and its foundation in universal intelligence on the other, were insisted on by Leibinz. (1646-1716.)

Within a year of his death Huxley said: "I no longer wish to speak of anything as unknowable; I confess that I once made that mistake even to the waste of a capital U."

In "Science and Morals" Huxley says: "I understand the main tenet of materialism to be that there is nothing in the universe but matter and force. . . . This I heartily disbelieve. . . . In the first place, as I have already hinted, it seems to me pretty plain that there is a third thing in the universe, to wit, consciousness, which, in the hardness of my heart or head I cannot see to be matter or force, or any conceivable modification of either, however intimately the manifestations of the phenomena of consciousness may be connected with the phenomena known as matter and force."

With matter in its grossest forms originating from and resolvable back into the ether, and with force originating in vortex motion, Huxley, had he lived long enough, would have found less difficulty in co-ordinating matter, force and consciousness, and in arriving at that divine and hence intelligent unity from which all diversity has emanated.

We have boundless space; universal substance; universal energy; universal intelligence, and universal consciousness. Space is thus the "all-container"; and all these are *One*. Boundless: Infinite, omnipresent, etc. Are not these the terms everywhere applied to Divinity? In seeking the key to Nature, science has stumbled upon the pathway to God.

"The entire process of ascending evolution appears to be dependent on the presence of mind; that is, consciousness, in the successive stages, from the simple to the complex."— PROFESSOR COPE.

"One continuous substance filling all space, which can vibrate as light, which can be sheared into positive and negative electricity, which in whirls constitutes matter, and which transmits by continuity, and not by impact, every action and reaction of which matter is capable—this is the modern view of the ether and its functions."—Professor Lodge, of University College, Liverpool.

"Thought is a mode of motion which is either entirely of the ether, or which affects the ether as well as matter."—Prof. Ames, of Johns Hopkins University.

"I think we are very near to a discovery of a physical basis for immortality that will transform most all our thinking."—Professor Dolbear.

"Matter, therefore, is not only divine, but it is the crowning act of divine love and self-sacrifice. It is God, giving away himself for man to use, to enjoy, to govern."

"God has nothing but his own perfect substance to make worlds (and all that they contain) out of."—Calthrope.*

Thus the substance of the universe is the garment of God. A new and far more literal meaning attaches to the saying, "in Him we live, and move, and have our being"; and "He is in all, through all, and over all."

Now the essential characteristic of man is his persistent, conscious self-identity. In the midst of all his diverse elements, and his warring passions, he is still *One*. Herein is the "likeness" of God in the face of the diversity of nature, in which man is said to have been made.

Every universal principle or potency that man has conceived or apprehended in nature is epitomized in man.

If space is "a conditioned fullness" out of which all things emanate and into which they all return, and from which they can never be for an instant separated, even in thought, then is this source of substance and energy, and this fountain of life, an eternal fountain, not only the source of all, but eternally pervading all.

Hence derived, and partaking of its attributes, is the consciousness of man, the *noumenon,* the potency, of all the phenomena of life.

---

*The foregoing brief quotations are from a very interesting little volume by C. J. Stockwell—"New Modes of Thought."

For the first time in the history of modern thought, here is a basis for a concept of the human soul in perfect consonance with our concepts of Nature and Divinity, and what Professor Huxley designated as the aim of science, viz., to deduce the rational order that pervades the universe. Nature is no longer at cross-purposes with God, nor is man by nature at war with either God or Nature.

The theory of the "Struggle to preserve the species in the midst of a hostile environment" is found to be false, because wholly inadequate and self-contradictory. Science has swung clear around the circle and come back to God.

In this crude and imperfect outline of the outposts of science enough has been said perhaps to indicate the signs of the times and the line of progress.

In the foregoing Study of Man, written now nearly fifteen years ago, the general theorem will be found to lead logically to just these later concepts of science. The twofold process of evolution and involution; the twofold life of man as inhering in the natural and the spiritual, and the chapter on Polarity, and the underlying Magnetism, are all consistent with these later concepts, and designed to lead up to them. These views, and the whole general concept, were derived from the Secret Doctrine of the Ancient Masters of Wisdom, unfolded to modern students by H. P. Blavatsky, to whose writings and instructions I owe more than any words of mine can ever express. The search for the soul is neither more nor less than a problem in the study of the conditions and changes in individual consciousness. This problem is unfolded and elaborated in the "Secret Doctrine" of H. P. Blavatsky. Whenever modern students are done with contempt prior to investigation, they will find the Secret Doctrine not only in full accord with the outposts and latest concepts of science, but they will find the whole problem of individual and race evolution, the nature of the soul, and the way of illumination at least fully outlined. Then will this wholly misunderstood and therefore misinterpreted messenger of *those who know* be measured by her mission, and judged by her work. As to what that verdict will be the present writer has no shadow of doubt, for it is already indicated in the signs of the times, in the recognition of the wisdom of the ancients, and guaranteed by that principle of justice innate in the soul of man.

In the closing chapter on the New Psychology it should be borne in mind that, what the problems of physical science are as related to the concept of space, such also are the problems of psychology as related to consciousness.

The *noumenon* of the phenomenal world, or cosmos; that is, the *no thing* from which all things emanate, is Space, in which God and Nature meet as One.

The *noumenon* in the intelligent life and varied experience of man is consciousness. This is the source of that involution, that eternal and inexhaustible fountain of Life, Intelligence and Love so often referred to in the foregoing Study of Man. Therefore, we shall comprehend both man and Nature just so far as we apprehend God. Here lies that "pre-established harmony" conceived by Leibinz, and that "rational order" referred to by Huxley. Here not only Science and Philosophy, but also Theology, meet as *One.**

Note: To call the views herein expressed "pantheism," neither defines them nor disposes of them, as many simple souls seem to imagine. In the first place, *which* pantheism, for scarcely less than a dozen different varieties might be named, each depending on the proportion in which the idea of God and the idea of Nature enter into the concept. The reluctance experienced by many good people in extending their idea of God from the personal (anthropomorphic) to the universal is well known. Yet all we know about "person" is essentially a limitation, and may even be a delusion. Personam—literally, a mask. The outward "person," "body," "mask"—conceals the real individual. Now, how, in this personal sense, can we apprehend God? Humanity, *as a whole,* personifies God: and as every star in space may contain other humanities, this is about as near the idea of an infinite personality as the mind can go. God personifies itself in the aggregate humanity. The whole humanity *masks* God.

CHAPTER XVII.

THE NEW PSYCHOLOGY.

The searchlight of science is rapidly penetrating many hitherto obscure fields of investigation, and presenting everywhere problems to be solved, even though the solution may be deferred. That the investigator is cautious and non-committal often shows that he is altogether sincere, so long as he really reserves judgment and does not prejudge either way.

Psychology is really the latest field to be thus explored. First, because religious belief or blind faith had already pre-empted the domain; and second, because of the exceeding complexity of the subject and the difficulties in the way of formulated results.

The "higher criticism" in the realm of religion has helped to pave the way by clearing up many historical problems, and by dissipating many dogmas in anthropology and cosmogenesis religion has thus been driven back to its legitimate domain in the spiritual life of man. The real problem of the soul is thus faced by both science and religion, in a distinct form, as never before perhaps in the life of the race.

It is true, here as elsewhere, that a problem clearly stated and well defined is already in the way of solution.

The question clearly stated is this: Is there any way, any method of research by which man may derive certain knowledge as to the existence, powers, and destiny of his own soul?

In previous chapters it has been shown that all real knowledge comes by individual experience, and can come in no other way. Religious knowledge is derived through religious experience. It is not superstition generated by the emotions of hope or fear, nor yet intellectual belief born of tradition or dogma, but an actual spiritual experience, wherein there is a breaking through of barriers that separate the higher elements of man's nature from the Universal Spirit and the Divine Intelligence that is above and beyond him. This is abundantly illustrated and demonstrated for all time by Prof. William James' "Varieties of Religious Experience."

So also with Scientific Knowledge of Psychology. To be real knowledge for anyone it must be derived from psychological experience. Outside of this, science may formulate theories or expound a philosophy of the soul, and may derive these from the actual experience of certain individuals, and we may even grant that the theories are true and the philosophy correct, yet for all this they are not real knowledge except for him who actually had the psychological experience, and forever must remain theoretical or conceptual for all others.

Psychological knowledge, for me, must be the result of the experience of my own conscious intelligent life, and cannot be determined by what I think or believe regarding such experience in the life of others.

Now the New Psychology may be said, in a very broad way, to refer to and to be the result of a large group of psychological experiences among a large number of individuals. As a body of knowledge, if any such term can by courtesy be applied to it at all, it is vague, empirical, and often contradictory. Dealing, as it undoubtedly does, with actual experiences, the motive that incites it is generally selfish or time-serving, and hence the result is seldom a clear perception of truth or a discernment of the underlying law. The average scientist ridicules these experiences, designates them as superstitions, or attempts to explain them away, or to deny them altogether. Prof. William James is a notable exception at this point. The individual who is convinced that he has gotten rid of a troublesome or painful disease, or whose life has become serene and happy through a psychological experience, is not disturbed in the slightest degree by this hostile or contemptuous attitude of modern science, and he is perfectly right in his position. However he may misinterpret the phenomena, or misspell his philosophy, his experience remains valid for him for all time. The *fact* is bound by no man's theory, and if fact and theory disagree, so much the worse for the *theory,* not for the fact.

It may thus be seen that the New Psychology is altogether in the formative stage, and that the scientist and the empirical masses are still wide of the real philosophy. Of the two classes, however, the empiric who has had actual experience is far nearer the truth.

The way of research that may lead to certain knowledge of the soul is, therefore, solely along the lines of actual experience of the individual.

What then is "experience?" It is *self-realization*—the recognition of that which actually occurs to the conscious self-identity of man. The character of the experience must depend upon the faculties or elements in man's nature that are involved. We experience pain and pleasure, joy and sorrow, and thus learn to recognize and to know the conditions upon which they depend, and so to avoid the one and to secure the other. This is knowledge derived from experience.

The ordinary experiences of man are largely related to the world of things; they occur in space and time through the avenues of sense in the physical body. But there is another realm in the conscious life of man where the senses are in abeyance; where the outer world of things is forgotten and for the time non-existent, and where space and time are lost in the realization of the immensity and the blessedness of Being. Prof. James declares such an experience to be as valid and as incontrovertible as are ordi-

nary experiences in time, sense and matter to ordinary individuals. In certain instances they have been the result of
striving through blind aspiration or religious zeal and devotion, with no apprehension of the psychical process or law
involved. Indeed, such instances as are generally known
more often have occurred in that way. A moment's reflection, however, will convince any intelligent student of psychology that there must be both a psychological process and
a psychological law underlying all such experiences.

The first thing observable in all such cases is the subordination of the physical senses and the relinquishment to
God of the personal will. Self-renunciation is the first step.
Thus has it been with the Mystics, the Saints, the religious
enthusiasts of all ages.

Prof. James designates these experiences as related to
the sub-conscious self. They are rather supra-conscious.
They transcend the ordinary experiences of the conscious-
self, instead of falling below them.

Without this group of experiences no Scriptures would
ever have been written; no such thing as Inspiration been
known; no religion ever have existed. Here lie the valid
spiritual experiences of man—that union with God, that
death to the world realized by the Saints and Mystics of all
ages.

It may be observed in passing that in the annals of spiritualism and hypnotism may be found many valid phenomena definitely related to those just referred to, but generally
fragmentary and incomplete. As psychical phenomena these
are valid, but as experiences to the individual they are not
only valueless, but positively pernicious and demoralizing.
In every instance mediumship and hypnotism dominate the
will of the subject; both are obscessions, just so far or in
whatsoever degree they exist. They therefore promote degeneracy and not evolution.

The dominance of the will by any hypnotist who is either
wholly ignorant or utterly regardless of the after-effects

upon his subject, and the surrender of the will to any passing "spirit," made ignorantly and voluntarily by the medium,
differ radically from that surrender to God of the mystic, in
which there is a conscious abnegation of the whole lower
nature, and an aspiration for spiritual light, leading, and
knowledge of God. No passing elemental, no earth-bound
spirit, no disembodied saint can for a moment satisfy the aspiration of the true mystic. Nothing but the Highest can
satisfy his aspiring soul. Even here, if the passions are
strong, and the lusts of the flesh unsubdued, obscession has
often been the result. The science of the soul, while cognizant of all these facts and processes, avoids all these pitfalls.
Self-possession through self-conquest is the first step. The
student thus avoids that weakening of the will seen in the
medium and the hypnotic subject, and equally avoids that
ecstatic emotion or frenzy of religious zeal seen in the
fanatic. All of these empirical processes serve to cloud the
intelligence and obscure the vision of the soul. The result
is often a relapse from ecstatic vision into licentiousness, to
be followed by remorse and despair, and even suicide. It
all depends in these cases on the previous life of the ecstatic and the extent to which self-conquest has been carried.

The foregoing suggestions may serve as illustrations,
and at the same time show how a knowledge of the soul in
its higher offices and spiritual planes ought not to be sought.
Spiritualists, Christian Scientists, and many other modern
cults talk and write very glibly of "Philosophy." In the
earlier chapters of the "Study of Man" philosophy has been
shown to be "the discernment of the rational order that pervades the universe." Huxley placed this as the ultimate aim
of science, and it is equally the beginning of all true philosophy. It is an intelligent conception of the *Synthetic Whole*.
Such bare assertions as "All is God," or "All is Mind," contain not a single element of real philosophy. They are even
devoid of common sense. They ignore the facts of common

experience, confuse the mind, and obscure the perception of truth, regardless of the fact that empirical effects, even in the direction desired, viz., the promotion of health, may and often do result.

A valid experience ought to promote the evolution of the individual and give understanding to the intelligence of man. Thus the whole realm of man's conscious life will be illumined; thus the facts of experience will lead to a science of life, and to a philosophy of the soul. Such juggling with concepts as those to which I have referred lead precisely in the opposite direction, and to designate them as "philosophy" is simply absurd. Against the facts or experiences involved I have nothing to urge, but confusion and nescience can only result.

It may thus be seen in what a chaotic state the New Psychology is involved. Prof. Henry James' *Gifford Lectures* offer the most hopeful outlook at the present time, the most fertile and promising oasis in this desert of the human understanding, this Simoon of psychical phenomena.

In the ancient mysteries of Initiation the candidate was first "worthy and well qualified," and then "duly and truly prepared." Anyone having any adequate conception of what genuine Initiation or Illumination really means must see from the very nature of the case that these rules of the Greater Mysteries are derived from a deep knowledge of the nature of man, of the laws that underlie the human soul, and the conditions of its higher evolution. They are like all other laws of Nature or Divinity, the same yesterday, today, and forever.

The intelligence of man may clearly discern that these laws exist, and at the same time be equally sure that his knowledge, though by no means complete, nevertheless discerns and conforms to the synthetic whole. That is to say, it is synthetic and in rational order as far as it goes. There may be gaps in his experience, but each new experience will fall naturally and spontaneously into its proper place in that order predetermined by the universal synthesis or rational order of the universe. It is thus that man may derive a knowledge of nature, a knowledge of God, and a knowledge of his own soul. This knowledge, thus derived, is synonymous with the higher evolution of man. This is the true psychology—a knowledge of the soul derived from actual experience through the spiritual faculties and powers of man.

In the "Secret Doctrine" of H. P. Blavatsky the philosophy upon which both cosmic and human evolution proceed is clearly defined and briefly epitomized. Each principle and plane of consciousness in man is there related to its corresponding principle and plane in cosmos. A rational order is thus revealed in that synthetic whole of which man is a part. From first to last the present "Study of Man" aims to be rather suggestive than dogmatic, and to lead logically to the real synthesis, rather than systematically formulating it.

The problem may be here suggested, however. The quest for the higher knowledge consists in the recognition by the individual of the basic principles in his own conscious life, and in the dominance, guidance, selection and use of the powers of his own being toward a predetermined result.

To intelligently discern his own powers and possibilities, to discover the line of least resistance and the method of highest use, and to make these conform to the attainment of his highest ideal is the aim. In the language of modern evolution this is: to develop within the individual the knowledge and the capacity (derived from experience) to conform to, or to control any and every change in, or condition of, his environment, and so immediately to adjust the personal to the universal, either by acquiescence or dominance of the new condition.

This means, in the strictest sense, and in the highest degree, knowledge and power; *i. e.,* Evolution.

The first step in this process is Introspection, or self-analysis. Thus may the individual come to *know himself—*

what he has been, what he is, and what he really desires to become.

If now he has conceived a high ideal, not as to success in life, or the applause of men, but as to what he would intrinsically become as a rational intelligence or a living soul, he may practically wipe off the slate up to date. Henceforth Desire and Will in him may be supreme, and lead him inevitably to the goal of his ideal. He may indeed have to struggle against old habits, but these he may dominate in a day *if he wills.*

Gradually he will gain self-control and surrender of lower aims, lower appetites and passions; this, if he has strongly desired and clearly conceived his ideal. He will find the realm of his own consciousness to be his own *kingdom,* and that he can transform it into heaven or hell, as he *wills.* At every step the conquest of the lower will mean induction into the higher realm of conscious experience. He will find that he can exclude the lower and mount to the higher, and that the one process includes the other; each supplements and assists the other.

Consciousness to man is the all-container, and *Will* is his primary endowment. Will and desire are the two poles of the motor power in him. Aspiration, discrimination, and the Ideal are the very essence of his intelligence— a "ray" from that Divine Intelligence which is the source of his being and the fountain of his life.

Having by degrees become master of the realm of his own consciousness, he will find this realm, this kingdom of the soul, expanding. His higher, spiritual powers, under the law of all nature, and all life will become synchronous with the Universal Intelligence, and faculties hitherto latent in him will begin to open and function on their own spiritual plane. The law here is the same as on the lower physical plane, for it is the same on all planes. It is the principle of synchronous vibration and universal harmony. It is exact, mathematical, absolute. It is the recognition of this law, and its application, that progressively promotes evolution, and from apprehension leads, at last, to its comprehension. The result is knowledge and power derived through experience.

As the consciousness of man thus compasses the world of thought and the world of things, and is alike rooted by the law of his being in the spiritual and the natural, the process above suggested may be seen to be a normal evolution. If there are no lapses in the will and aspiration of the aspirant he will presently find a new world opening to him. Serene, steadfast, master of self, he will realize that there is no bar to his progress other than he himself imposes, and no limit to the knowledge and power within his grasp. He will learn to know the spiritual world precisely as he has known and may continue to know the natural.

It may thus, perhaps, be discerned that the New Psychology is barely the suggestion of the True Psychology; that the constructive period in its unfoldment and realizaton has not yet dawned on the average understanding of man.

If the foregoing brief and imperfect outline shall make it seem rational, apprehensible, possible, it is all that the present work contemplates. Beyond that it has ever been, and must still be a matter of individual effort and individual experience. Nothing can be truer, or more philosophical, than the saying that each must work out his own salvation.

It requires but a glance to show that the highest types of the human race, those who have combined spiritual knowledge with spiritual power, and crowned both with divine compassion and beneficence to man, have developed along just these lines. These may have followed an inner intuition, and been indifferent to, or even incapable of formulating the underlying law, or the clear philosophy upon which the whole process proceeds, just as a natural musician may discern and execute the divine harmonies, though ignorant of the laws of consonance or harmony; or, as one like Colburn may perform the most astonishing feats with numbers before he has learned the rules of mathematics.

The present writer is acquainted with two individuals, one of whom spontaneously, like the natural musician, and one by design, effort, and instruction, has attained to open vision and spiritual illumination. In either case, the bounds of the body, of sense (physical), of time, and ordinary consciousness are entirely transcended, with the spiritual world looming up like a newly discovered continent or a New World.

As object lessons these are of great interest, for they justify to the last detail that philosophy of the higher evolution of man which is both natural and obtainable, and which is suggested and outlined in the foregoing pages.

It would be strange indeed if there were no such royal highway of the soul open to man. If Divine Intelligence had "made man after its image," implanted in the soul the longing for light and certain knowledge, and yet left its attainment forever impossible, that were Tantalus indeed, and the handiwork of eternal hatred, rather than of Infinite Love and Divine Intelligence.

May we not hope that the New Psychology is the promise and the dawn of the True Psychology?

THE GENIUS OF FREEMASONRY AND THE TWENTIETH CENTURY CRUSADE

By J. D. Buck 33°

Volume I. Supplemental Harmonic Series

This book is at once a *sign* and a *summons* to every Masonic Brother who loves his Country, his Home, his Family, and the Craft of which he is an honored member.

Every Brother Mason worthy of the name, however exalted or humble he may be, owes it to himself to know what this book contains.

Masonry is facing the most vital and crucial issue in its history.

The call is for *men of courage.*

Are you willing to stand up and be counted? If not, you WILL be after you have read this splendid book.

Price, cloth, $1.00; Morocco, $2.00. Postpaid.

CONSTRUCTIVE PSYCHOLOGY

THE BUILDING OF CHARACTER BY PERSONAL EFFORT

By J. D. Buck, M. D.

Volume III.   Supplemental Harmonic Series

The Lewiston Journal says, "Dr. Buck has performed a distinct service to humanity in giving this book to the world."

It is a work of deep thought and profound erudition which, as a supplement to the Harmonic Series, is invaluable. The world is now thinking along these lines as never before, and in the great work of settling the Psychic problem Dr. Buck is doing his full share. This little book is a mine of information and the blazing of another pathway to that higher life that lies just beyond the portals of the tomb.

The thoughtful and intelligent student will find no necessity for consulting libraries, philosophies, authorities, or theologies, helpful as these may be; for this little book turns him back upon himself and undertakes to make exceedingly plain those few simple principles by which he may adjust himself by personal effort and establish harmonious relations to God, to Nature and to his fellow man.

You will make no mistake in adding this to your private library.

Beautifully bound in blue cloth.   Price $1.00 Postpaid.

MYSTIC MASONRY

By J. D. Buck, M. D., 33°

Volume V. Supplemental Harmonic Series

"*Mystic masonry*" has done much to awaken interest in the Science and Symbolism of Freemasonry. There has long been, among thoughtful Masons, a strong impression that the sublime truths of Masonry do not lie on the surface, and that they are rather concealed in the ritual of the Lodge than openly disclosed and explained.

Commendations of "*mystic masonry*" have as often come from non-Masonic readers as from members of the Craft. There is no reliable history as to how and when the Institution of Modern Freemasonry came into existence, nor who was the author of its ritual or its philosophy. From the first it has undergone no essential change, and every Mason is pledged to preserve its ancient landmarks unaltered. So perfect, however, is this sublime institution that, after two hundred years of progress in the most fruitful era of human evolution, Masonry is still abreast of the times and up to the most advanced spirit of the age. No wonder, then, it is called a "*divine institution*". The secrets of Freemasonry pertain solely to the ritual and the rights and benefits of the lodge, while the philosophy is open to the world at large.

The author of "*mystic masonry*" has outlined the philosophy of Masonry in this little book and explained many of the ancient symbols.

The book is, therefore, quite apprehensible to the non-Masonic reader, as nothing essential to the understanding of the philosophy is concealed, and it is designed to be a contribution to the knowledge of psychology and the uplift of the human race.

Cloth, 260 pages. Price $1.00. Postpaid.

THE LOST WORD FOUND

By J. D. Buck, 33°

Volume II.   Harmonic Booklet Series

This is unquestionably the finest, strongest and most compelling bit of work done by this well-known Physician, Mason and Philosophic writer, Dr. J. D. Buck, 33°.

Such a pronunciamento, message and invitation as are encompassed in these fifty pages rarely find their way into public print.   Such "Lectures" and such "Instruc_ tions" are rarely passed beyond that Fraternity which is founded upon the legend of the Lost Word.

To him "who hath eyes to see" this is a Signal from the Watch-tower.

To him "who hath ears to hear" it is a clarion call from "refreshment to labor".

For him who has courage it invites to Discovery.

For him who is seeking it is a guide and a light.

For him who is ready, who is "duly and truly prepared," it is a sign and a Summons that *The Great Work* and the *Lost Word* are at hand.

Bound in Blue Silk Cloth.   Price 50 cents Postpaid.

MODERN WORLD MOVEMENTS

By J. D. Buck, M. D., F. T. S., F. G. S., etc.

INTRODUCTION

By TK

Volume VII. Supplemental Harmonic Series

Ever since the time the three Text-Books of Natural Science were presented to the public, there has been an ever increasing demand for information concerning the Theosophical Society and the Great School, and the relations they sustain (if any) to each other, and concerning the *"Masters"* back of the two movements; and there has come to us an almost endless chain of subsidiary questions growing out of the main subject, involving much correspondence.

We have done our best to answer these questions; but to comply fully with these inquiries would require more time than we are able to give them. We have, therefore, requested Dr. J. D. Buck to aid us in satisfying these demands.

Dr. Buck is doubtless better qualified to give this data than anyone in this country; for he is one of the oldest living members of the T. S.; was personally acquainted and intimately associated with the founders of the Theosophical Society; prominent in its councils and active in its service; and is, today, the owner of the most unique and valuable psychological library in America, if not in the world.

He speaks, therefore, from the viewpoint of an "Inner" member of the Theosophical Society and his words will command the respectful consideration of every Student of this Subject.

He is also an active, accredited Student of the School of Natural Science, and, therefore in position to speak of and for the Great School as well as for the Theosophical Society. Price $1.00. Postpaid.

The book is now in press.

THE SOUL AND SEX IN EDUCATION

By J. D. Buck, M. D., 33°

This book is from the pen of J. D. Buck, author of "Mystic Masonry", "Constructive Psychology", "A Study of Man", and other works with which our readers are familiar.

This is not one of our publications, but it falls so directly in line with the Educational Work of the Great School in this field, and the Literature of this Movement, that it is of special value to every Student and Friend of the Work in America. We are therefore keeping it in stock and are glad to furnish it to our patrons and Friends.

Dr. Buck has probably never written a more useful book, and the many problems which so often confront and perplex us regarding "Love, Marriage, Celibacy and Divorce" or the problem of Sex, have never been more concretely and intelligently discussed and elucidated than in this volume.

This book should be of special value to every Friend and Student of the Great Work in America.

Bound in cloth. Price $1.25 Postpaid.